14-120_1138

STATIC
RELAYS

for
Electronic
Circuits

Based on the
Static Relays Symposium
sponsored by
ELECTRONIC COMPONENTS
RESEARCH DEPARTMENT
U. S. ARMY SIGNAL RESEARCH
AND DEVELOPMENT LABORATORY

STATIC
RELAYS

for
Electronic
Circuits

Edited by
RICHARD F. BLAKE

President
Transistor Devices Inc.

Formerly
Manager
Electronics Department
Aero-Space Division
Walter Kidde & Company

ENGINEERING PUBLISHERS
ELIZABETH, NEW JERSEY

Trade Distributors:

REINHOLD PUBLISHING CORPORATION
NEW YORK

CHAPMAN & HALL, LTD.
LONDON

Preface

The static relay has passed through its initial stage of being a clever curiosity. The basic design techniques have been established, the armed forces are actively supporting static relay programs, and several companies are in production. Static relay types include those for dry circuits, for control, power contactors, and circuit breakers. They avoid many of the inherent problems of mechanical relays, such as contact bounce, and typically have extremely fast response, long life and high resistance to shock and vibration. However, the static relay is not generally a direct replacement for the mechanical relay and in many applications it is not competitive. Rather, it is an additional type of relay which expands the field of relay applications.

The static relay is now in the transitional period between initial development and general acceptance. As more application information is disseminated and as production costs are reduced, the static relay will undoubtedly become one of the basic components regularly used by the equipment designer.

Since the static relay concept is relatively new there are several answers to, "What is a static relay?" The broadest definition is: "A static relay is an integral packaged unit marketed as a component to perform a relay-like function." Some authorities add the requirements of (1) snap action, (2) electrical isolation between control and contact circuits, and (3) no crosstalk between control and contact circuits. In an effort to set up uniform standards, representatives of the armed forces are preparing a series of general specifications for static relays. The purpose of this book is to present a comprehensive summary of the present state of the art for the equipment designer, the student, and the static relay designer.

Richard F. Blake
Editor

Contents

1. Static Relay Concept*

As time passes we are repeatedly reminded of the tremendous strides which the modern sciences are taking. We have seen the development of incredibly complex electronic systems. In the comparatively few years since World War II, systems have been developed which are capable of

> Solving intricate mathematical problems with amazing speeds,
> Transmitting thousands of messages over long distances in a few minutes,
> Guiding and controlling missiles to their destinations,
> Detecting, tracking, and interpreting the signals of satellite transmitters as they explore the intimate details of outer space.

The heart of these advanced systems is, invariably, an electronic nerve center which must receive a continuous flow of signal intelligence from many sources within the system. These nerve centers then sort and analyze these signals and, at the proper time, issue commands to the many local control substations where they are translated by the individual control elements. These elements, or control devices, then provide the final link which energizes the functional circuit into action. At such points in the system we will most generally find a circuit "making" and "breaking" device.

If we examine this device we will most likely find an electromagnetic driving motor to which is coupled an assembly of electrical contact elements comprising what we call a relay.

For many years the relay underwent only incremental changes in performance and design principle. However, with the advent of World War II, and the new exacting demands of military usage, a

*This material was prepared by A. W. Rogers of the Office of the Chief Signal Officer for presentation at the Static Relays Symposium.

major metamorphosis occurred in the electromagnetic relay. This evolution has been continuous and has yielded the rugged, versatile, high quality military-grade relays which we know today.

However, in any technical field, today's solution is immediately succeeded by tomorrow's problem. Many of the expanded systems requirements of the immediate future exceed the realizable capabilities of the electromagnetic relay. In addition, the problems of critical adjustment, close mechanical tolerances, complex mechanical linkages, and electromagnetic inefficiencies place practical limitations on the relay's sensitivity, economy, and ultimate reliability.

Fortunately, while these problems of the electromechanical relay were being attacked, tremendous advances were taking place in the allied field of logic switching. With the rapid development of semiconductor, ferromagnetic, and other solid-state elements, which exhibited switching characteristics, the speed, versatility, and efficiency of logic circuitry was greatly extended. With the availability of this new tool, systems designers incorporated solid-state control circuitry in their equipments with increasing frequency. However, as with any new art, lacking appropriate disciplines, individual solutions to problems met with varying degrees of success.

It was in response to this need for developing a design discipline, and in recognition of tomorrow's critical and demanding control device requirements, that the static relay was evolved.

Just what is a static relay? In its simple definition it might be described as a device which is capable of performing electronic circuit control functions in a manner which is similar to that of an electromagnetic relay, without the use of moving parts or elements. From this simple definition we can extract three dominant characteristics:

First, the static relay employs no moving parts. This, of course, is apparent from the connotation "static."

Second, it is a device. It is not a single element which must be associated with supporting electronic parts to perform a switching function. Nor is it simply an assemblage of passive and active electronic parts, performing a "relay-like" function, which is integrated within an equipment. It is an entity in itself. It is an integral, packaged aggregate of electronic parts, exhibiting individual characteristics, and capable of performing specific circuit switching functions. It is readily identifiable, interchangeable, and replaceable as a unit.

Third, the static relay performs its function in a "relay-like" manner. It does, therefore, provide discrete ON and OFF states, which are determined by the actuating signal condition. It provides high signal-to-load power and ON to OFF impedance ratios. Its ON and OFF states are reached within prescribed signal limits and intermediate impedance levels do not appear at the load terminals. Electrical isolation between the signal circuit and load circuits, and vice versa are provided. Finally, design principles are such that a number of individual load circuits may be switched from a common signal, without intercircuit coupling.

I must be careful not to paint too bright a picture for the future of the static relay, as I do not visualize the obsolescence of the electromagnetic relay. I feel that the static relay technology will provide the stimulus of healthy competition. Competition has always been a major factor in the achievement of scientific progress. With continuing development in both fields, I feel confident that ultimately two distinct classes of functional circuit control components will be established. As a result, each will find the greatest application to those areas to which its peculiar advantages are best suited.

2. Review of Semiconductor Regenerative Switching Devices

I. A. LESK

Semiconductor Products Department
General Electric Company
Syracuse, New York

Within the past several years there have appeared many semi-conductor negative resistance switching devices, working on different principles, having different characteristics, and bearing a variety of names. The purpose of this chapter is to review those devices that can exhibit useful regenerative switching characteristics in the vicinity of room temperature, and provide a qualitative description of their construction and operation. Only static switching devices are discussed, and of these, only those holding promise for practical application are included. Amplifying devices (transistors held within rated voltages and currents) will likewise not be discussed even though they may always be made to exhibit negative resistance regions of limited extent in suitable circuits.

Semiconductor devices utilizing internal regeneration to produce characteristics suitable for switching applications are grouped according to the number of PN junctions they have. In each case, the characteristic of interest has high and low impedance regions separated by a negative resistance. Switching is accomplished electrically by exceeding the peak point in the case of two-terminal devices, and by the same means or by triggering for the three-terminal units. In many cases, switching may also be produced by a non-electronic stimulus such as heat, light, or nuclear radiation. Structures making exclusive or partial use of whisker or surface barrier contacts are omitted because this type of contact exhibits PN junction characteristics, and all the important devices made in this way have been reproduced in junction form.

4

It is expected that many of the negative resistance devices discussed in this chapter, together with others yet to be conceived, will become almost as widely used as the transistor itself. Aside from this expected utility, there are other reasons why device and circuit designers should have an overall familiarity with regenerative semiconductor switches. Large negative resistance regions occur during the operation of amplifying devices in many circuits if voltage specifications are exceeded (Sections 3.1. and 3.2). Those concerned with application and characterization of devices must recognize these possibilities. Further, similiarities of the PN junction region geometries between many of the regenerative switches and well behaved diodes and triodes require the device designer to consider the possibility of inadvertent switching in his units.

1. DEVICES WITHOUT PN JUNCTIONS

1.1. Thermistor (1)*

The thermistor (thermally sensitive resistor) is a piece of semiconducting material, often of the oxide type, with ohmic contacts applied to opposite sides. The bulk material is chosen to have a large negative temperature coefficient of resistivity. A typical resistance-temperature curve and a common sample shape are shown in Fig. 1. As the current through a thermistor is increased (in either direction), the voltage rises according to Ohm's Law. If more current is drawn, power dissipated in the thermistor increases its temperature and hence decreases its resistance. The point is eventually reached where the decrease in resistance due to the heating caused by an increase in current is so large that the voltage actually drops, and a negative resistance results, Fig. 1 (right). Since regeneration in the thermistor involves heat flow, switching speeds are slow compared to most other semiconductor devices.

1.2. Bulk Avalanche Diode (2)

The bulk avalanche diode consists of a single type of semiconductor having a discontinuity in impurity concentration. This is indicated as an N^+N boundary in Fig. 2 the N^+ region having a much larger donor concentration than the N region. The cross-hatched end regions denote ohmic contacts.

For a small applied bias about the origin, the current-voltage characteristic is ohmic. As the voltage is raised, the electric field in the N region increases to high values and the mobility decreases. Hence, a nonlinearity of the characteristic occurs as

---

*Numbers in parentheses refer to references at end of chapter.

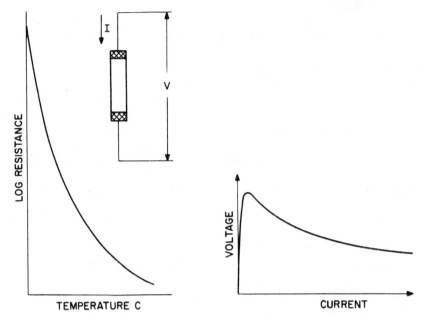

Fig. 1. The thermistor and its characteristics. The resistance-temperature characteristic is at the left, and the voltage-current characteristic showing the effect of selfheating is at the right.

shown. As the electron velocity reached its limiting value in the N region, a high incremental resistance region in the voltage-current characteristic occurs. Near the peak voltage, bulk avalanche multiplication in the N region occurs. The resulting additional electrons and holes are separated by the electric field, the holes being swept towards the N region ohmic contact. The build-up of hole concentration near this ohmic contact is partially compensated by electrons, resulting in resistivity modulation and hence a decrease in electric field there. Hence, the current-voltage

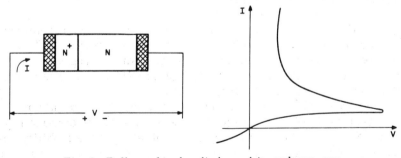

Fig. 2. Bulk avalanche diode and its voltage-current characteristic.

characteristic displays a negative resistance region. The higher the current, the larger the compensated minority carrier modulated region, the lower the voltage. At a sufficiently high current, the avalanche is concentrated in a thin layer of the N region adjacent to the N^+ region, holes being injected into the N region just as though a PN junction were present.

The bulk avalanche diode is a fast switching device because of the large electric field, and because there is no PN junction to impede minority carrier removal during turnoff.

2. DEVICES WITH ONE PN JUNCTION

2.1. Unijunction Transistor (3)

The unijunction transistor (double-base diode), Fig. 3, can be considered simply as a semiconductor resistor with ohmic end contacts designated Base 1 and Base 2. Between the end contacts, a PN junction is formed. In the circuit of Fig. 3, if the Base 2 contact is disconnected, $(I_B = 0)$, the input characteristics are much like those of a PN junction diode. For negative values of V_j, the PN junction is reverse biased and only a very small leakage current flows. When V_j is positive, the junction is forward biased and a low impedance region results. The voltage drop in this forward-biased region is larger than in the case of a PN junction diode of comparable area because of the relatively larger junction-Base 1 distance.

Now consider the situation with a constant interbase potential V_{B_2} applied. The bar of semiconductor between base contacts acts as a potential divider, presenting a positive voltage at the N-type side of the PN junction. Hence, as V_j is made slightly positive, the junction still has a reverse bias, and still only a small leakage

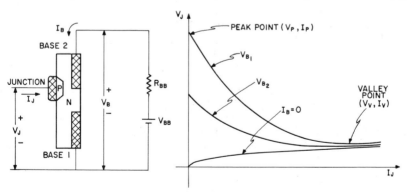

Fig. 3. Unijunction transistor and its bias scheme (left), and set of junction characteristics.

$$V_{B1} > V_{B2} > 0$$

current flows. As V_j is made more positive, it approaches its peak point at a value equal to the lowest potential on the N-type side of the junction, which occurs on the side of the junction nearest Base 1. A slight increase in V_j results in the injection of holes into the N-type bar at the side of the junction nearest Base 1. The holes are driven by the interbase electric field in the direction of Base 1. This increases the hole concentration in the junction-Base 1 region; the electron concentration also increases to preserve charge neutrality. As I_j increases, the injected carrier concentration in the junction-Base 1 region exceeds the original thermal equilibrium value. This decreases the electrical resistivity in this region, forcing more of the interbase potential to appear in the junction-Base 2 region. The condition is soon reached whereby an increase in I_j, produces such a drop in junction-Base 1 region resistivity that the resulting potential shift in the bar lowers V_j, and a negative resistance region follows. The negative resistance region persists until V_j drops to a value near the curve for $I_B = 0$, and then gives way to a region of small positive resistance.

A larger interbase potential, V_{B_1} in Fig. 3, results in a larger negative resistance region. The ratio of peak point voltage to interbase voltage is a constant, the standoff ratio N.

$$V_P/V_B = N$$

The peak point current may be positive (silicon devices, or germanium devices at low temperatures) or negative (generally at higher temperatures where the leakage current is larger). The valley point voltage and current both increase somewhat with V_B.

2.2. Tunnel Diode (4)

The tunnel diode consists of a PN junction in which the transition from one type of semiconductor to the other is abrupt, and in which both N-type and P-type regions have such large impurity concentrations that they are degenerate. Under such conditions, for small reverse or forward voltages, electrons flow by quantum mechanical tunneling through the junction barrier, giving rise to large currents, AOB in Fig. 4. For a reverse bias (opposite to polarity shown in Fig. 4), region AO, current is carried mainly by electrons tunneling from the P-type to the N-type region. For a slight forward bias, current is carried primarily by electrons tunneling through the barrier from the N-type to the P-type region. In the higher forward voltage region CD, the tunnel diode behaves much like a normal PN junction diode, and has a current rapidly rising with voltage. In this region, at least part of the current is carried by electrons injected from the N-type to the P-type region, and holes injected in the other direction over the PN junction barrier. Tunneling current decreases with voltage in the region BC because the overlapping of energy banks, due to degenerate conditions on both sides of the junction, is becoming very small. The current at the point C is usually greater than that carried by a normal diode at the same voltage.

Tunnel diodes are very fast because the mechanism responsible for their operation, quantum mechanical tunneling, takes place with essentially the speed of light. The switching speed, which is

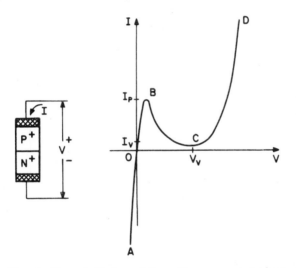

Fig. 4. Tunnel diode and its voltage-current characteristic.

limited by the parasitic junction capacitance, is the fastest of any semiconductor device. The tunnel diode, because of the stability of its negative resistance characteristic, its speed, low noise, and simplicity of operation, is also used in amplifier applications.

2.3. Unipolar Transistor

Usually there is no negative resistance in a unipolar transistor characteristic, and when it does appear (due perhaps to a non-ohmic drain contact) it is not suitably large for switching. Operation of a unipolar transistor is briefly explained here because it enters into the operation of another device (Section 3.3).

The unipolar (field effect) transistor, like the unijunction transistor, is essentially a semiconductor resistor between two ohmic contacts, designated the source and the drain, Fig. 5(a). It also has a PN junction formed on the semiconductor pellet between the end contacts. If the junction is reverse-biased, most of the potential drop is taken up in a space charge region that forms, extending from the PN boundary into the semiconductor pellet. To a first

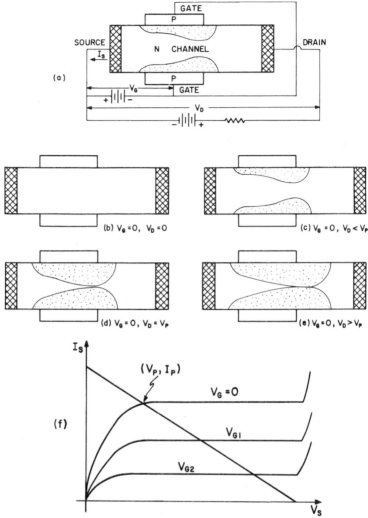

Fig. 5. Unipolar transistor and its bias scheme (a); space charge for different drain voltages with zero gate bias (b, c, d, and e); and at (f) a set of characteristics.

$$V_{G2} > V_{G1} > 0$$

approximation, there are no mobile current carriers in such a space charge region, and the high field in it is in such a direction as to exclude electrons in the semiconductor bar from entering. Hence, any space charge reduces the cross-sectional area of the pellet through which electron current flows, and raises the resistance between source and drain. Gate current is very small, comparable to the reverse leakage current in a PN junction diode.

Space charge and channel geometries for a zero gate bias condition are shown in Fig. 5, together with a set of electrical characteristics. In Fig. 5(b) is shown the unipolar transistor geometry, with no applied potentials. Maintaining a short circuit between source and gate ($V_G = 0$), and applying a voltage between source and drain of the polarity shown, electrons flow down the N-type semiconductor pellet from source to drain. A space charge region (shown dotted in Fig. 5c) spreads into the channel. If V_D is increased further, a condition is reached where the channel area is reduced to a very small value. This is called pinch off, at $V_D = V_P$. As V_D is increased past V_P, I_D increases very little until the avalanche voltage of the junction is reached. If a constant reverse bias had been applied to the gate (say V_G), then a smaller value of I_D would be required to produce the pinch off condition, Fig. 5f.

3. DEVICES WITH TWO PN JUNCTIONS

3.1. Avalanche Transistor

3.1.1. Device Controlled. Figure 6 shows the common emitter characteristics of a typical silicon transistor exhibiting avalanche switching. For zero base current, little collector current flows until V_{CE} is increased to the collector junction avalanche breakdown voltage. As avalanche breakdown of the collector junction allows more current to flow, current gain α increases. This increase of α with I_C is exhibited by almost all transistors. Because

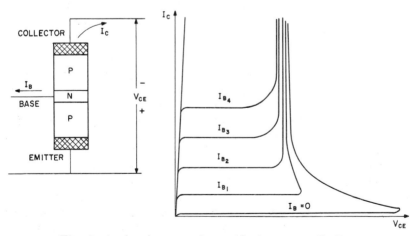

Fig. 6. Avalanche transistor (device controlled) together with its bias scheme at left, and the voltage-current characteristic at right.

$$I_{B5} > I_{B4} > I_{B3} > I_{B2} > I_{B1} > 0$$

no base current flows, the shape of the resulting voltage-current characteristic is determined by the equation $M\alpha = 1$, where M is the (voltage dependent) avalanche multiplication factor. The curve generally approaches a vertical asymptote, followed by a positive resistance region, because the increase of α with I_C approaches a maximum value and then decreases. If base current is drawn, part (I_{B_1}) or all (I_{B_2}, I_{B_3}, I_{B_3}) of the negative resistance region is removed.

3.1.2.   Circuit Controlled. (6) In the case of germanium transistors, collector junction leakage current and low level α are generally so high that the open base curve looks like that for I_{B_3} in Fig. 6. In this case, drawing a base current in reverse to that shown in Fig. 6 (right) can make the characteristic approach the lower curve of Fig. 6 (left).

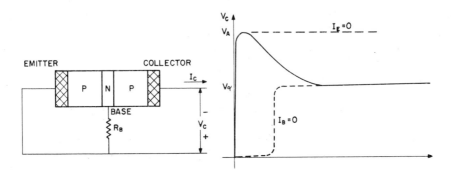

Fig. 7. Avalanche transistor (circuit controlled) at left, and its voltage-current characteristic at right.

Another circuit method of accomplishing the same result is shown in Fig. 7, left. In some cases, the transistor external base resistance is high enough so that R_B can be eliminated. For V_C less than the collector junction avalanche voltage V_A, most of the leakage current flows through R_B since the emitter junction resistance is very high at such a small current level. Avalanche breakdown at V_A allows more current to flow, most of it still through R_B. The resultant IR drop in R_B is in a direction to forward bias the emitter junction. The increase in emitter current is much larger than the base current that caused it because of the nonlinearity of the PN junction voltage-current characteristic. As I_C increases, a larger fraction of the current flows through the emitter, so that the voltage drops and approaches the $I_B = 0$ curve having a limiting voltage V_α determined by satisfying the equation $M\alpha = 1$ (where α varies slowly with I_C).

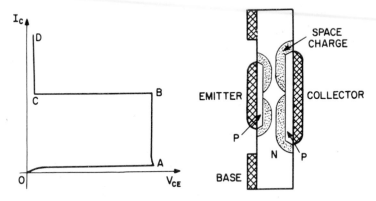

Fig. 8. Ring base transistor d-c switch. Voltage-current common-emitter characteristic for constant reverse emitter-base bias (left), and space charge configuration (right) in the base for region C-D.

3.2. Punch-Through Transistor (7)

When a reverse bias is applied to the collector junction, the space charge region in the base may extend to the emitter junction (punch-through) at a voltage below the avalanche breakdown. This effect, rather than avalanche breakdown, can be used to control the peak voltage points in Figs. 6 and 7. If the punch-through and avalanche voltages are about the same, the device is sometimes called a punch-through-avalanche transistor.

3.3 Ring Base Transistor DC Switch (8)

When NPN or PNP transistors of the ring base type (base contact forms a complete circle concentric with the emitter-collector central axis) are driven in the common emitter mode with a constant reverse voltage bias between emitter and base, then the characteristic shown in Fig. 8 (left) often results. Up to point B the curve looks normal, with the high resistance section OA followed by the avalanche breakdown region AB. The switching to a low impedance state is the result of a change in space charge configuration, as shown in Fig. 8 (right). When in region AB, the collector junction is in avalanche breakdown. Electrons flowing into the base from the avalanche region are largely excluded from the emitter because of its reverse bias, so they flow out the base. If the transistor design is such that emitter and collector space charge regions have almost met when the collector junction breaks down, then the base (electron) current flows through a narrow channel, much the same as in the unipolar transistor (Section 2.3). This lowers the potential at the center of the base, resulting eventually in a shift to the space charge geometry shown in Fig. 8 (right). In this mode, the device is operating as both a (bipolar) transistor and a unipolar transistor simultaneously. Current flow is constricted to a small channel, so burn-out is a problem in this type of switch.

3.4. Bar-Type Transistor Saturation Switch

If the base contact area of a bar-type transistor, Fig. 9 (left), is made very small, and the surface recombination velocity is made high, then the common emitter characteristics will show a negative resistance at higher current levels, Fig. 9 (right). This is due to a drop in current gain of the transistor when coming out of saturation. When saturated, both emitter and collector are

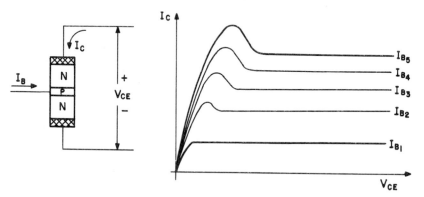

Fig. 9. Bar-type transistor saturation switch and its bias scheme (left), and (right) its character-istics. $I_{B5} > I_{B4} > I_{B3} > I_{B2} > I_{B1} > 0$

forward biased, so at high current levels the base resistance is lowered by resistivity modulation due to the injected carriers. When out of saturation, at the same current, only the emitter junction is forward biased, the average concentration of injected carriers in the base is reduced, so the level of resistivity modu-lation is lowered. The resultant larger base resistance causes an increased crowding of emitter current about the base contact, where surface recombination is effective in lowering the current gain.

4. DEVICES WITH THREE OR MORE P-N JUNCTIONS

4.1. Hook Collector Transistor (9)

The hook collector transistor is shown in Fig. 10 (top). Con-sider the PNPN type, and for an explanation of its operation assume a small increase of emitter (hole) current, which results in a slightly smaller increase of hole current flowing into the collector P-type region. Since this P-type region is electrically floating, carriers injected into it can leave only by flowing into either of its bounding N-type regions, or by recombining within it or at its surface with carriers of the opposite type. Both of the junctions bounding the P-type collector region act as barriers to hole flow out of it, so the holes reaching it are trapped in a potential minimum (hook). Their positive charge raises the potential in the hook region, allowing an electron current to flow from the collector N-type region, through the collector hook region, into the base. This electron flow accounts for practically all the increase

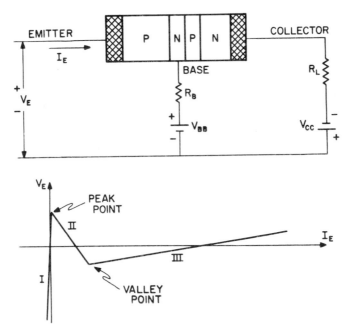

Fig. 10. Hook collector transistor in a circuit (top) for $\alpha > 1$ switching mode. An idealized characteristic is at the bottom.

in external collector current. The change in collector current is larger than the increase in emitter current used to produce it (i.e. $\alpha > 1$) because each hole trapped in the hook region can live long enough to result in the flow of many electrons across the hook.

Transistors having $\alpha > 1$ whenever the emitter junction is forward biased display negative resistance regions in several circuits. One of the most common is shown in Fig. 10 (top). The characteristics have been idealized into three straight line segments. In Region I, the emitter (also the collector) junction is reverse biased, so the input impedance is very high. At small positive emitter currents, a small increment in I_E results in a V_E increment approximately $(1 - \alpha) R_B$ times as large. Since $\alpha > 1$, this gives a negative resistance, Region II. At the valley point, current through the resistance R_L is so large that the collector junction bias is zero. At larger currents, in Region III, all of the transistor junctions are forward biased, so that the device

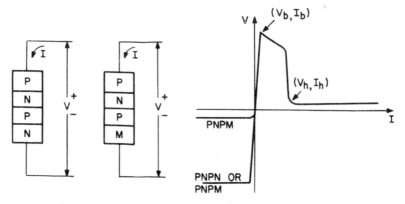

Fig. 11. PNPN diode (left), PNPM diode (center), and the voltage-current characteristic (right).

acts almost like a short circuit connecting the input with the two parallel circuit sections.

Transistors with $\alpha > 1$ tend to act as fast switches when going from Region I to Region III, perhaps due to the effects of the base electric field, which is partially in a direction to shorten the transit time of carriers from the emitter to the collector junction. The turn-off time (switching from Region III to Region I) is much longer because it lasts until the charge stored in the collector hook region has largely disappeared.

4.2. PNPN (and PNPM) Diode (10)

The PNPN diode is shown in Fig. 11 (left). Even though it is a two-terminal structure, there may be ascribed to it a current gain α just as if a lead were attached to one of the base regions. The current gain may be considered as the sum of the current gains of the PNP and NPN transistor sections. The main difference between the PNPN device and the hook collector structure (which looks identical in geometry, Section 4.1.) is that in the latter, current gain is greater than 1 for all positive values of emitter current, while in the former, current gain is less than unity at low currents and climbs above unity at higher currents. This is accomplished by control of geometry and characteristics of the four regions. For low voltages of the polarity shown, the reverse biased center junction limits current flow to a low value at which current gain is less than 1. As voltage is increased, the avalanche breakdown point is reached. Increasing current past the peak point results in an increasing current gain, so the voltage falls. (Section 3.1.1). At some current, the current gain increases to unity and beyond without the aid of avalanche multiplication, so that the voltage drops to a very low value, and a low impedance state results. For the reverse polarity of applied voltage, both end junctions are reverse biased, so that the characteristic follows a high impedance curve and breaks down at the sum of their avalanche voltages, Fig. 11 (right). If one end region is made metallic in nature to promote the drop of α at low currents, we have a PNPM diode, Fig. 11 (center). Its characteristic is much the same as that of a PNPN diode, except that for practical reasons, the inverse breakdown voltage is usually low.

PNPN (or PNPM) diodes can be made as very fast switches, and to cover a large range of current and voltage. They are sometimes called 4-layer diodes.

4.3. PNPN (and PNPM) Triode (11)

A lead (gate) attached to one of the base regions in a three PN junction diode switch may be used as a control electrode. The resulting structure, Fig. 12 (top), looks like a common emitter operated transistor. For zero gate current, the characteristic is like that of the equivalent two-terminal device, (Section 4.2). If gate current is drawn, a current I flows through the main switch structure just as in a transistor. Current gain α is increased by the increase in current I, so at some voltage below the center junction avalanche breakdown point the value of $M\alpha$ reaches unity (Section 3.1.1.) and current increases rapidly with voltage. A negative resistance region and a low impedance state follow. Figure 12 (bottom) shows a set of curves for increasingly large values of gate current. A sufficiently large gate current will remove practically all of the high impedance region (I_{G4} curve). Hence, with a suitable load line, switching occurs from the high resistance to the low resistance state because of high impedance region is lowered in voltage to below the load line by means of the gate current.

PNPN switches (controlled rectifiers) and PNPM switches (thyristors) are made in both low and high power ranges, some of them being very fast. Turn-on current ratios can be very large and, in some cases, appreciable turn-off current ratio is obtained in the lower current range.

Modifications on the basic PNPN design include structures in which two of the end regions are connected together (shorted

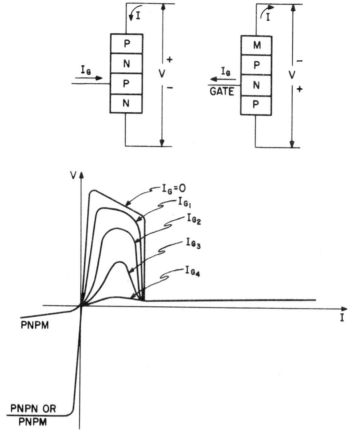

Fig. 12. PNPN triode (upper left), PNPM triode (upper right) and their bias schemes, and (bottom) gate controlled characteritics.

$$I_{G4} > I_{G3} > I_{G2} > I_{G1} > 0$$

emitter structure) and devices having a tunnel junction at one end. Both these changes result in superior switching characteristics.

4.4. NPNPN Symmetrical Switch (11)

The four PN junction switch is illustrated in Fig. 13 (left) for an NPNPN type, although the PNPNP device is analogous. The NPNPN switch can be made symmetrical, displaying the same characteristic for either polarity of bias, Fig. 13 (right). More efficient low resistance regions as well as other benefits are obtained by making both end PN junctions shorted-emitter or tunnel junction

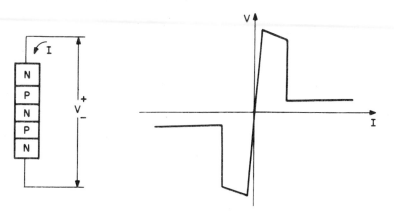

Fig. 13. NPNPN symmetrical switch (left) and its
voltage-current characteristic (right).

types. As in the case of PNPN switches, base leads may be used
to trigger switching.

REFERENCES

1. Becker, J. A., C. B. Green, and G. L. Pearson, Trans A.I.E.E., 65, 711 (1946).
2. Gunn, J. B., Proc. Phys. Soc. B, 69, 781 (1956).
3. Brown, S. R., and T. P. Sylvan, Electronic Design, Jan. 8 and Jan. 22, 1958.
4. Lesk, I. A., N. Holonyak Jr., U. S. Davidsohn, and M. W. Aarons, 1959 I.R.E. Wescon Convention Record, Part 3, p. 9.
5. Dacey, G. C., and I. M. Ross, B.S.T.J., 34, 1149 (1955).
6. Miller, S. L., and J. J. Ebers, B.S.T.J., 34, 883 (1955).
7. Beale, J. R. A., W. L. Stephenson, and E. Wolfendale, Proc. I.E.E., 104B, 394 (1957).
8. Thornton, C. G. and C. D. Simmons, I.R.E. Trans. Electron Devices, ED-5, 6 (1958).
9. Klein, M. and A. P. Kordalewski, I.B.M. Journal, 3, 377 (1959).
10. Lesk, I. A., I.R.E. Trans. Electron Devices, ED-6, 28 (1959).
11. Aldrich, R. W. and N. Holonyak, J.A.P., 30, 1819 (1959).

3. Technical Specifications for Static Relays

WILLIAM J. FONTANA
DANIEL L. WALK

U. S. Army Signal Research and
Development Laboratory
Fort Monmouth, New Jersey

With the evolution of the solid-state switching concept within the U. S. Army Signal Research and Development Laboratory (USASRDL) and other military and commercial research and development organizations, a new field of electronic circuit control and switching devices known as static relays has been generated. The technology which led to this class of component is primarily concerned with the development of integral multipurpose "black box" switching devices. These devices are capable of performing a variety of switching functions which are similar to, and in a manner compatible with, the switching modes generally associated with conventional electromagnetic "relay-like" devices. To justify their existence and live up to their promise, static relays should, among other things, be capable of performing these "relay-like" functions better and faster, and for longer periods of time than is possible with conventional relays. They should also perform their functions with greater reliability and, ultimately, in smaller volumes than the electromagnetic counterparts which they are intended to supplement. In so doing, it is important that static relays not introduce unexpected pecularities or vagaries of performance which might generate secondary effects—effects which can result in the introduction of new problems in system operation. Further, to insure compatibility with conventional devices, and be adaptable to systems use, their limits of performance over the entire range of military electrical, physical, and mechanical environments must be predictable and controlled.

With the growth of this "static relay" art, a number of prototype and sample models have recently become available. As a result, their integration into many current and future systems is a reality. In view of this, from the user's standpoint, a specification which would, at least initially, establish fundamental control criteria was considered essential. This specification would then necessarily be continually expanded and augmented as technology and usage increased. It was toward this objective that the USASRDL undertook the development of Signal Corps Technical Requirements SCL-6316, "Static Relays."

Because of the number of potential static relay design approaches available for the accomplishment of specific switching functions, it was initially determined that a performance-type specification was most desirable. Such a specification could then accomplish three fundamental purposes. It could:

1. Establish the limits and ranges of performance of individual devices, while still defining classes of functions or usage best adapted to Static Relay design concepts.

2. Be sufficiently non-restrictive to permit the solution of various switching problems by any suitable static circuit design and element technique.

3. Provide the systems designer with operational limits and capabilities of individual items. This would permit their incorporation into systems with adequate assurance of satisfactory operation.

At the present time, transistor and silicon controlled rectifier types of static relays have probably reached the most advanced state of development, and are most readily available. They have, as a result, received the greatest attention from military and other potential users. It is conceivable, however, that with further development many of the other physical concepts which fundamentally provide switching modes of operation, such as magnetic amplifiers, and ferromagnetic, electrotransducer, electro-optic and cryogenic elements may gain greater acceptance and utility in the future static relay concept.

However, to limit the scope of investigation and provide a realistic document based on available devices, the specification was designed around, and particularly directed to, the class of static relay employing junction type semiconductors as its output or "contact" elements. Since this specification does not specifically exclude other "contact" elements, it is hoped that, despite its somewhat restricted scope, it will still serve as a basic foundation around which further documentation in this area can be developed. Meanwhile, it will provide some much needed guidelines for the definition, procurement, and use of static relays for experimental and development purposes.

To determine the requirements to be specified, the test procedures to be employed, and the operational precautions to be incorporated in the document, a number of prototype devices were analyzed and characterized under many circuit and test conditions. These prototypes, which employed various transistor and silicon controlled rectifier output switching elements, comprised commercially developed and USASRDL-built experimental models, as well as models devised and fabricated under a USASRDL sponsored static relay development contract with Walter Kidde & Company. Certain predictions concerning the expected performance and limitations of the USASRDL-sponsored items could be made prior to actual tests. In the case of the commercially developed devices, however, circuit analysis was not always possible. Because of the proprietary nature of the designs, and the natural reluctance of some organizations to provide information, complete circuit details were not always available. As these items were studied and test data evolved, a general behavior pattern developed. It was observed that certain significant characteristics were common to many of the types studied. Among the undesirable characteristics observed, which were considered to require specification attention, were:

The lack of inherent isolation between input and output circuits. With specific designs inductively coupled circuits were provided to accomplish this isolation. In such cases, however, the inter-circuit coupling of the various elements in the device could then limit the degree of isolation obtained.

Depending on the character of the active elements and circuit techniques employed and the range of output-to-input impedance ratios which resulted, varying degrees of load to signal feed-through and interference existed.

Many devices required the application of d-c and/or a-c power from external sources. This standby power was then converted within the device. As a result, electromagnetic radiation at either or both input or output terminals was present.

The energy required by the input circuit to actuate the output varied widely, depending on fundamental device design. Although comparable signal sensitivity and operational capability existed under steady-state conditions, the requirements for pulse operation were, to a major extent, determined by the input reactance of the circuit.

Multipole devices generally involved the replication of output circuitry with a common actuating element. The resultant coupling between individual circuits gave rise to potential crosstalk problems.

As a result of the studying of these and other design characteristics, the extensive testing of available models, the analysis of circuit components, construction, and packaging techniques used, and the evaluation of general application requirements, a series of specification criteria were evolved.

Fundamentally, the purpose of the requirements contained in the resultant specification is to control and define many of the desirable, as well as the undesirable, characteristics of the static relay. Since individual designs displayed various specific characteristic behaviors, as many controls as practical were included in the specification body.

Although complete analysis of the specification details is beyond the scope of this presentation, we should like to discuss briefly portions of the requirements and some of the techniques employed to determine the degree of conformance or non-conformance of individual devices to such requirements.

To fulfill the basic objective of the document it was decided to employ the Tri-Service, General Electro-Magnetic Relay Specification, MIL-R-5757 as the cadre of the new document. MIL-R-5757 is an omnibus specification wherein definitions, procedures, and general requirements only, form the specification body. Detail requirements for specific classes and types are contained in appended requirement sheets. This general format lent itself admirably to the document under development. With such a format, as technology advances, items could be readily added, modified, or deleted without major specification revision. Because of the rapidly changing static relay art, such flexibility will provide a significant advantage.

The initial step in the development of the specification was the establishment of definitions applicable to static relays in general. For practical reasons, phraseology and terminology commonly associated with magnetic relays, which could define pertinent functions and parameters with a minimum of ambiguity, were used as far as possible. For example, the static relay is defined as:

"A bistable solid-state device having an output circuit which can be actuated by a polarized signal to the input circuit. The output circuit shall be so arranged that it will present a high impedance to the flow of current in an inactive condition and a low impedance in its active state."

In a further definition, that of a null-seeking relay, the following conventional phraseology is employed:

"A multicontact static relay of double-throw configuration and a stable center-off position. Either side of the double-throw contact can be activated by and for the duration of the polar actuating signal."

Similarly, definitions for other relay configurations, operate and release time, and leakage current were established along conventional relay lines.

A number of the common electronic component requirements such as life, insulation resistance, dielectric strength, shock, vibration, thermal stability, etc., were specified. These requirements are based on conventional MIL-STD-202, and MIL-R-5757 tests and test procedures. The electrical operating characteristics of static relays, however, required the use of procedures which are, in terms of relay methodology, unconventional. Such requirements were evolved and techniques for the evaluation of device performance developed.

Briefly and broadly defined, these requirements consist of the following:

Sensitivity. The minimum signal energy required to cause operation of the relay.

Overdrive. The ability of the relay to perform its function under excessive signal conditions.

Snap Action. The ability of the relay to switch from one state to the other without intermediate output impedance conditions or "jitter."

Saturation Resistance. The resistance of the output circuit in its active state.

Leakage Current. The stand-by current of the active elements (as distinguished from insulation resistance).

Effect of Transients. The stability of the device under load and line transient conditions.

Overload Capacity. The ability of the output, or load circuit, to withstand moderate overloads for short periods of time.

Cross Talk. The electrical coupling between multiple output circuits.

Interference. The electromagnetic radiation generated within the device.

The specification discusses these elements in detail, and provides test set-ups for their evaluation. For illustrative purposes three such requirements are discussed here:

The sensitivity or energy required to accomplish the output circuit function is specified under three conditions: (a) DC signal input, (b) repetitive pulse operation, and (c) single pulse or "one-shot" operation. The first two requirements need no elaboration. It might be well, however, to mention the "one-shot" or single pulse sensitivity. In the test evolved to evaluate this characteristic, the relay is driven by a series of individual rectangular pulses whose pulse widths are equal to one-half the period of the rated operating frequency of the device. With suitable discharge of input circuitry between applied pulses, the pulse amplitude is increased in discrete steps until device actuation occurs. This amplitude is then taken as a measure of the single pulse sensitivity of the device under test. It is interesting to note that variations as high as 20 percent were observed among the three sensitivity measurement conditions for individual relays.

To evaluate the snap action of the device, a variable d-c voltage is applied to the input circuit. The relay is then "teased" by slowly raising and lowering this voltage around the operating threshold value while the output state is continuously observed on a suitable oscilloscope. Although not quantitatively specified, discrete "on" and "off" conditions are required.

To determine the crosstalk susceptibility of multipole devices, an audio frequency signal whose amplitude is equal to the open circuit voltage rating is applied to one contact set at a time, with the relay in the unenergized state. The signal induced in each of the output circuits is then measured.

In general, the test procedures defined by the specification, and the associated test set-up diagrams, do not require highly sophisticated equipment. Practically all the requirements of the specification can be tested for by using conventional laboratory instrumentation. With the exception of two items, only conventional vacuum tube voltmeters, power supplies, loads, ovens, and other reasonably common laboratory equipments are required.

Of the two "special" items, one is the oscilloscope. It should be of the calibrated dual-channel high-speed type with an accurate time base. In addition, it must either be equipped with a recording camera or be of the infinite retentivity type. The other item required is a variable-rate rectangular-pulse signal generator capable of providing single externally triggered pulses of adjustable amplitude.

APPENDIX

SIGNAL CORPS
TECHNICAL
REQUIREMENT

SCL-6316
5 January 1960

STATIC RELAYS*

1. SCOPE

1.1 Scope. This document together with the listed technical specification provides for procurement of static relays for relay-like applications to be used in experimental and developmental models of U.S. Army Ground Signal and Guided Missile equipment.

1.2 Classification.

1.2.1 Type designation. Static relays shall be designed by specific purpose and power rating until such devices reach proportions necessitating an identification system.

*This material is presented as advance technical information for development purposes only and it is not to be considered as an official document concerned in any way with any Government purchase which may be in progress.

2. APPLICABLE DOCUMENTS

2.1 The specifications, standards and drawings listed in technical requirements SCL-6200 of the issue in effect on the date of invitation for bids shall form a part of these requirements.

3. REQUIREMENTS

3.1 Definitions.

3.1.1 Static relay. A bistable solid state device having an output circuit which can be actuated by a polarized signal to an input circuit. The output circuit shall be so arranged that it will present a high impedance to the flow of current in its inactive condition and a low impedance in its active state.

3.1.1.1 General purpose relay. A static relay which can be activated by and for the duration of the actuating signal.

3.1.1.2 Null seeking relay. A multicontact static relay of double-throw configuration and a stable center off position. Either side of the double-throw contact can be activated by and for the duration of the polar actuating signal.

3.1.1.3 Latch relay. A static relay of double-throw configuration (no center off) which has bistable contact characteristics with or without continuous signal.

3.1.1.4 Differential relay. A summing, double-input, static relay which can be actuated by the polar signal resulting from the algebraic addition of dual inputs.

3.1.2 Snap action. That property exhibited by a device having no intermediate stable conduction states between activated and non-activated contact levels.

3.1.3 Maximum leakage current. The maximum leakage occurring at the output contacts in the non-conductive state at rated voltage and with a 2000-ohm resistor shunting the input terminals.

3.1.4. Operate and release time. The operate time is defined as the time lapse between the application of a step function input signal and the 90 percent value of rated contact current. The release time is defined as the time lapse between the trailing edge of the step function and the 10 percent value of rated contact current. Both values shall be measured under resistive load conditions. (See Fig. 1).

3.2 Requirements.

3.2.1 Terminals.

3.2.1.1 Solder terminals. Outside solder terminals may be of any shape provided dimensional limits are met. The solder terminal shall be capable of accepting normal wire of the size specified. Terminals for sealed relays shall protrude through the seal. All terminals shall be so designed that the specified wire size may be mechanically secured prior to soldering.

3.2.1.2 Screw terminals. Outside screw terminals or inside terminals when repairable units are used shall be supplied with one nut, two flat washers and one lock washer. The nut shall remain

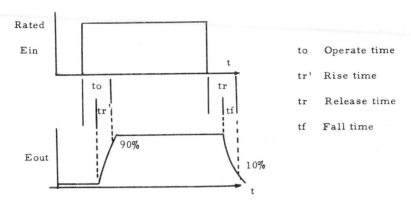

to   Operate time

tr'   Rise time

tr   Release time

tf   Fall time

Fig. 1. Timing factors.

engaged by at least three threads when backed off three complete turns from a position with all parts tightened in place.

3.2.2 <u>Threaded parts</u>. Threaded parts shall be Class 2 fit in accordance with Handbook H-28.

3.2.3 <u>Case</u>. The case shall not be used for electrical ground but may be used as part of the thermal sink.

3.2.4 <u>Workmanship</u>. Static relays shall be manufactured and processed in accordance with good design and sound practice techniques.

3.2.5 <u>Soldering</u>. When soldering is employed the use of flux shall be avoided whenever possible. If the use of flux is warranted, only non-corrosive fluxes shall be used unless it can be shown that non-destructive methods can eliminate all traces of corrosive elements after soldering. Soldering shall be in accordance with Specifications QQ-S-561 and QQ-S-571.

3.2.6 <u>Marking</u>.

3.2.6.1 <u>Identification marking</u>. The following information shall

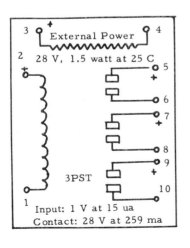

Fig. 2. Contact, input, and external power terminal symbolism.

be permanently and legibly marked in accordance with MIL-STD-130 on an unobstructed surface of the static relay or on the chassis of open units.

a. Technical Specification Sheets numbers as assigned by USASRDL.

b. Rated sensitivity.

c. Standby power (voltage and current).

d. Contact rating (voltage and current).

e. Manufacturer's name or symbol and catalog designation.

f. Contact and input symbolism with necessary terminal numbers per example shown by Fig. 2.

3.2.7 Moisture resistance. When tested as specified in 4.1 there shall be no evidence of deterioration as determined by visual inspection and insulation resistance and dielectric strength tests.

3.2.8 Dielectric strength. When tested as specified in 4.2 the relays shall withstand the application of the specified potential without damage or breakdown.

3.2.9 Insulation resistance. When measured as specified in 4.3 the insulation resistance between all insulated terminals and case or frame shall be 1000 megohms or greater.

3.2.10 Electrical characteristics.

3.2.10.1 Sensitivity. The static relays shall operate and release with snap-action at the specified voltage and current input when tested as specified in 4.4.1.

3.2.10.2 Input overdrive. When tested as specified in 4.4.3 the specified increase in signal voltage shall not have an adverse effect on the operation of the contact circuit.

3.2.10.3 Snap action. There shall be no intermediate stable conduction state between off and full on when tested in accordance with 4.4.2.

3.2.10.4 Operate and release time. Static relays shall operate and release within the specified time limits when tested in accordance with 4.4.4.

3.2.10.5 Saturation resistance. When tested as specified in 4.4.5 the saturation resistance of the output circuit shall not exceed the rated maximum.

3.2.10.6 Leakage current. The leakage current shall not exceed the rated maximum specified on the detail specification sheet when tested in accordance with 4.4.6.

3.2.10.7 Power dissipation. The relay power dissipation in the energized or de-energized state shall not exceed that specified when tested in accordance with 4.4.7.

3.2.10.8 Contact overload. The relays shall operate normally when tested in accordance with 4.4.8.

3.2.10.9 Stand-by power supply transients. When the relay is tested in accordance with 4.4.9, the contact shall not deviate from its de-activated state. If a normally closed contact requires standby power to maintain that state, then with the application of stand-by power that contact will switch to the closed state with snap action.

3.2.10.10 Cross-talk. In a multicontact relay variations of one contact load shall not adversely effect other contacts when tested in accordance with 4.4.10.

3.2.10.11 Minimum input duration. When the relay is tested as described in 4.4.11, the contact switching shall not be completed until the pulse width exceeds 60 percent of the specified minimum value.

3.2.10.12 Power supply interference. The average AC voltage from the source shall not exceed the specified value when the relay is tested as specified in accordance with 4.5.12.

3.2.10.13 External power variation. The contacts shall not deviate from the actuated state when the external power is varied ±20 percent under rated input signal as specified in accordance with 4.4.14.

3.2.11 Vibration. When the relay is tested as specified in 4.5.14, there shall be no evidence of loosening of parts.

3.2.12 Shock. When the relay is tested as specified in 4.5.15, there shall be no evidence of loosening of parts.

3.2.13 Temperature operation. When relays are tested in accordance with 4.5.16, the operating characteristics shall remain as specified.

3.2.14 Thermal shock. When hermetically sealed relays are tested as specified in 4.5.17, there shall be no evidence of mechanical damage. Electrical characteristics shall be measured immediately following the test and shall remain as specified.

3.2.15 Thermal stability. The temperature of the saturated device shall not exceed its rated thermal rise and the relay shall respond to 100 percent of the input pulses when tested in accordance with 4.5.18.

4. QUALITY ASSURANCE PROVISIONS

4.1 Moisture resistance. Static relays shall be tested in accordance with Method 106 of MIL-STD-202. The following details and exceptions shall apply:

a. Mounting. On a corrosion resistant metal panel by normal mounting means.

b. Initial measurement. Insulation resistance.

c. Polarization. Omit.

d. Final Measurements. Upon completion of Step 6 of the final cycle, insulation resistance shall be measured. After a 24-hour drying period at a relative humidity of 50 ±5 percent, measurements of insulation resistance, dielectric strength and operating characteristics shall be made.

4.2 Dielectric strength. The terminals of electrically isolated portions of the static relay shall be shorted and a potential of 500

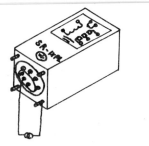

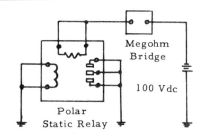

Fig. 3. Dielectric strength.

Fig. 4. Insulation resistance.
Note: Additional terminals
grounded.

volt rms 60 cycle shall be applied between those isolated portions
and the case. The potential shall be maintained for one minute
(see Fig. 3).

4.3 <u>Insulation resistance</u>. The insulation resistance shall be
measured at a dc potential of 100 volts. The voltage shall be applied for one minute between shorted input and shorted output terminals and including the power supply terminals if the device utilizes external power (see Fig. 4).

4.4 <u>Electrical characteristics</u>.

4.4.1 <u>Sensitivity</u>.

4.4.1.1 <u>DC static sensitivity</u>. The input voltage shall be increased from zero until the contacts operate. The input shall then
be increased to the maximum rated input and decreased until the
contacts are deactivated. For this test, the contacts shall switch
rated maximum load and a suitable voltmeter shall be used to
monitor the contact action (see Fig. 5).

4.4.1.2 <u>Repetitive pulse dc sensitivity</u>. The input voltage shall
be raised from zero until the contacts operate under a repetitive
signal at rated frequency. The input shall then be increased to the
maximum rated input and decreased until the contacts no longer
operate. The contacts shall switch rated maximum load and a suitable oscilloscope shall be used to monitor the contact action. The

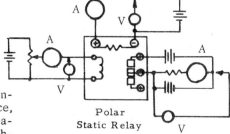

Fig. 5. DC static sensitivity, DC input overdrive, saturation resistance,
leakage current and power dissipation. Use reversing switch for latching.

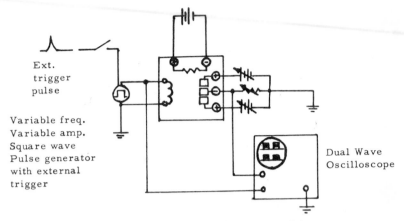

Ext.
trigger
pulse

Variable freq.
Variable amp.
Square wave
Pulse generator
with external
trigger

Dual Wave
Oscilloscope

Fig. 6. Single pulse sensitivity, repetitive pulse sensitivity, input overdrive, contact overload, contact rise and fall time, operate and release time, and minimum input duration.

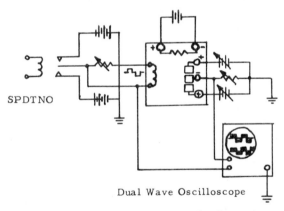

SPDTNO

Dual Wave Oscilloscope

Fig. 6b. This method used for latch static relays if no polar signal generator is available. For high speeds use alternate static relay. Repetitive pulse sensitivity, input overdrive, contact overload, contact rise and fall time, and operate and release time.

minimum input signal to activate the contacts shall not be greater than the maximum of 4.4.1.1 (Fig. 6) (for latching, see Fig. 6b).

4.4.1.3 Single-pulsed dc sensitivity. The input voltage shall be raised from zero until the contacts operate under a single dc pulse. The input shall be raised in steps and the input shall be shorted after each incremental increase. The contacts shall switch rated maximum load and a suitable long duration trace shall be used to monitor the contact action. The minimum pulse amplitude shall not exceed the maximum specified in 4.4.1.1. or 4.4.1.2. The pulse width shall be one half the period of the rated frequency. (See Fig. 6).

4.4.2 <u>Snap action</u>. Employing the circuit shown in Fig. 7, the input voltage shall be raised from zero by means of resistor R_2 with R_1 set at maximum resistance until the relay contacts are actuated. The resistance of R_1 shall be decreased until the relay contacts are no longer activated and R_1 shall be increased slowly until the contacts again actuate. The contacts shall be observed by a suitable oscilloscope or ammeter for indication of positive snap action.

4.4.3 <u>Input overdrive</u>. The input power shall be raised to a value 10 db above the rated operate power and tests conducted as out-

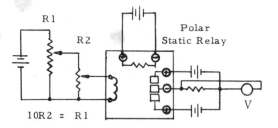

Fig. 7. Snap action.

lined in 4.4.1.1, 4.4.1.2, and 4.4.1.3. The contacts shall carry rated maximum load and suitable means shall be used to monitor the contact action. (Figs. 5, 6, and 6b.)

4.4.4 <u>Operate and release times</u>. The relay shall be excited by a rectangular pulse at 10 percent above rated static input voltage of 4.4.1.1. This test will be conducted at 1/4 rated frequency and rated frequency and 50 percent duty cycle at specified source impedance. The input and contact waveforms shall be displayed on an accurate time base, dual trace oscilloscope. (See Fig. 6 or 6b).

4.4.5 <u>Saturation resistance</u>. The saturation resistance shall be measured across the contacts while switching rated maximum load as in 4.3.1.1 (Fig. 5).

4.4.6 <u>Leakage current</u>. The leakage current of the contact circuit shall be measured at rated contact voltage with input shunted with a 2000 ohm resistor at 25 C (see Fig. 5).

4.4.7 <u>Power dissipation</u>. The power dissipated shall be observed in both the activated and deactivated states. (See Fig. 5).

4.4.8 <u>Contact overload</u>. The relay shall be tested at 10 percent above rated power at rated frequency for a period of 200 cycles. This shall be accomplished by first raising the voltage at rated current for 100 cycles and then raising the current at rated voltage for 100 cycles to obtain the 10 percent power overlead. (See Fig. 6 or 6b).

4.4.9 <u>Standby power transients</u>. With the input terminals shorted, the external power shall be manually switched off and on while the contact is observed for deviation (see Fig. 8).

4.4.10 <u>Cross talk</u>. Multiple contact relays where one or more contacts may be energized will be tested by imposing an audio signal of rms voltage equal to the rated voltage on the contacts of one non-actuated circuit while monitoring the remaining contacts. There shall be a 66 db isolation between all isolation contacts (see Fig. 9).

4.4.11 <u>Minimum input durations</u>. The static relay shall be driven by a rectangular single pulse at 10 percent above rated static input at the rated frequency pulse period. The pulse width or duty cycle shall be decreased until the relay fails to close. (See Fig. 6 or 6b).

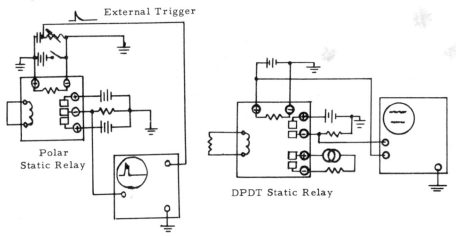

Fig. 8. Stand-by power transients.   Fig. 9. Cross talk.

4.4.12 <u>Generated internal interference</u>. Static relays containing internal power converters or inverters shall be monitored at all external terminals for excessive electrical radiation. This test shall be performed while the static relay is in the unactivated state and activated state by the use of a high speed sensitive oscilloscope and a high resistance dc meter such as a VTVM.

    a. With external power on the input terminals shall be monitored with: open input signal terminals, 10K ohm across input signal terminals and 1K across input signal terminals.

    b. With 10 percent above rated input dc signal voltage, the input, and external power terminals shall be monitored by a sensitive, high speed oscilloscope with rated resistive load across the contact terminals. (See Fig. 10).

4.4.13 <u>Contact rise and fall times</u>. The contacts shall be activated by symmetrical rectangular pulses at rated pulse width and 10 percent above rated static input voltage. The rise time as defined in Figure 4 shall not be more than 3 percent of the rated pulse duration when viewed on an accurate time base oscilloscope.

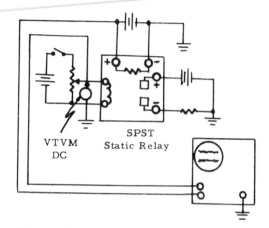

Fig. 10. Generated internal interference.

The fall time as defined by Figure 4 shall not be more than 5 percent of the rated pulse duration. (See Fig. 6 or 6b).

4.4.14 <u>External power variation</u>. Static relays requiring external power shall be tested by variations of ±20 percent with no deviation of the contacts while activated by rated input signal. (See Fig. 11).

4.5 <u>Vibration</u>. Static relays shall be tested while rigidly mounted and subjected to simple harmonic motion in accordance with test condition C of Method 204 of MIL-STD-202.

4.6 <u>Shock</u>. Shock testing shall be in accordance with Method 202 of MIL-STD-202.

4.7 <u>Thermal stability</u>. The static relay shall be continuously energized carrying rated voltage and current at the high temperature extreme for not less than 2 hours. The contact switching

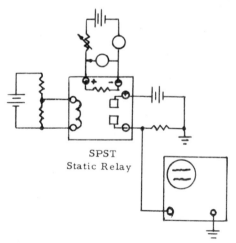

Fig. 11. External power variation.

characteristics and sensitivity shall be observed. Immediately following high temperature operation, the leakage current of the contact circuit shall be measured at rated voltage. The same test shall be applied to the relay at low temperature specified.

4.8 <u>Thermal shock</u>. Hermetically sealed static relays shall be subjected alternately to 3 cycles of immersion in tap water at 85 C and 0 C for a duration of 20 minutes per immersion. Not more than 5 seconds shall elapse between hot and cold immersions.

4.9 <u>Time test</u>. The static relay shall be driven at its maximum operate frequency, the contacts switching rated voltage and current for a period of 48 hours at 25 C ambient. The driving source shall be a rectangular pulse generator. The total input and output signals shall be counted on electronic counters. The ambient temperature of the device shall be monitored throughout the test.

5. PREPARATION FOR DELIVERY

5.1 The items covered by this specification shall be packaged, packed and marked in accordance with the bid request and contract.

6. NOTES

6.1 The following Signal Corps Technical Specification Sheets (TSS) form a part of this specification.

SCL-6316/A   Requirement Format for Special Purpose Static Relays
SCL-6316/1   Sensitive SPST Static Relay
SCL-6316/2   Polar Static Relay DPDT
SCL-6316/3   Sensitive SPST Static Relay
SCL-6316/4   Small Signal SPST Static Relay

TECHNICAL SPECIFICATION SHEET, SCL-6316/A

REQUIREMENT FORMAT FOR SPECIAL PURPOSE STATIC RELAYS

1. Physical Requirements

End view	Input, contact, and external power symbolism
Side view	Additional views if appropriate

Description
a. Weight   lb
b. Terminal size: AWG and Type

2. Electrical Requirements
   a. Input
      (1) Maximum actuate signal _____ma at _____volts
      (2) Minimum release signal _____ ma at _____volts
      (3) Overdrive protection (25 C)_____volts
      (4) Maximum electrical interference_____mv
      (5) Input wave forms___step function _____ sinusoidal
                      spike_____
   b. Contacts   _____ latching
                                            _____ polar
      (1) Arrangement:_____pole_____throw_____other
      (2) Rated resistive load_____ amps at_____ volts___ac
              _____dc
      (3) Reactive load:_____volts steady state, ____volts peak
              transient_____amps steady state,_____
              amps peak transient
      (4) Multiple contact:_____isolated pairs_____common
              terminal_____
      (5) Maximum permissible leakage_____ ma at_____C
      (6) Saturation resistance at rated load_____ohms_____
      (7) Operate maximum speed_____cycles per second
      (8) Maximum electrical interference_____ mv
   c. External power
      (1) Standby voltage available_____volts _____
      (2) Maximum internal interference_____ mv _____
   d. Other requirements
      (1) Input distortion (max) _____ % _____
      (2) Ambient temperature extremes_____to_____C
      (3) Life: (a) continuous_____cycles
                     (b) intermittent 50% duty cycle_____hours
      (4) Isolation
          (a)__dc__   Input to output   db
                           output to input   db
          (b)__ac__   input to output   db
                           output to input   db

3. Mechanical Requirements

   a. Shock_____G's
   b. Dielectric _____volts, not applicable_____

4. Additional Requirements

   Specify any special requirements not covered above.

TECHNICAL SPECIFICATION SHEET, SCL-6316/1

SENSITIVE SPST STATIC RELAY

1. Physical Requirements

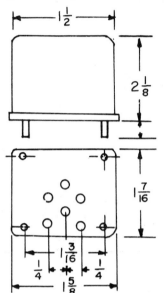

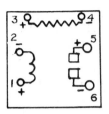

Dimensions in inches
Tolerance: ±1/16 in.
Weight: 0.24 lb
Terminals: Teflon imbedded
0.0625-in. solder studs

2. Electrical Characteristics

a. Input
(1) Maximum actuate signal: 17 ua at 1.28 volt (-55 C)
(2) Minimum release signal: 1.5 ua at 0.50 volt (+85 C)
(3) Overdrive protection: 10 volt (25 C)
(4) Maximum electrical interference: 90 Millivolt (25 C)
(5) Input wave forms X step function X sinusoidal X spike

b. Contacts
(1) Arrangement: Single pole, single throw___latch
___polar
___other_____
(2) Rated resistive load: 0.25 amp at 28 volts DC
(3) Maximum leakage: 20 ua at (+85 C)
(4) Saturation resistance: 8.3 ohms at (+85 C) 0.25 amp
(5) Operate speed maximum: 5kc
(6) Maximum electrical interference: 550 millivolts

c. External power
(1) Stand-by power: 60 ma at 28 volts
(2) Maximum electrical interference: 90 millivolts

d. Other characteristics
  (1) Ambient temperature operation: -55 C to +85 C
  (2) Life: (a) continuous 30×10^6 operations
            (b) intermittent 10,000 hours
  (3) Isolation AC input to output 60 db
                output to input 60 db

TECHNICAL SPECIFICATION SHEET SCL-6316/2

POLAR STATIC RELAY DPDT

1. Physical Requirement

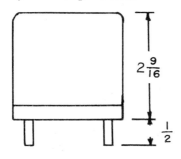

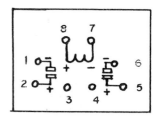

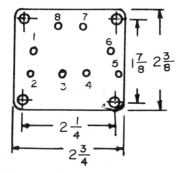

Dimensions in inches
Tolerance: ±1/16 in.
Weight: 0.63 lb
Terminals: Teflon imbedded
0.0625-in. solder studs

2. Electrical Characteristics

  a. Input
    (1) Maximum actuating signal 1.85 volts at 13 ua
    (2) Minimum releasing signal 0.80 volts at 3.1 ua
    (3) Overdrive protection (25 C) 10 volts
    (4) Maximum electrical interference 150 mv (25 C)
    (5) Input waveform <u>X</u> step, <u>X</u> sinusoidal,____spike

  b. Contacts
    (1) Arrangement - double pole, double throw, polar
    (2) Rated resistive load - 250 ma, 28 volts dc
    (3) Reactive load

(4) Multiple contact - isolated pair
(5) Maximum leakage - 3.60 ua (+85 C)
(6) Saturation resistance at rated load - 1.36 ohms
(7) Maximum operating speed - 5 kc
(8) Maximum electrical interference - 550 mv (25 C)

  c. External power
    (1) Standby voltage - 28 volts dc
    (2) Maximum internal interference - 550 mv (25 C)

  d. Other
    (1) Ambient temperature -55 C to +85 C
    (2) Life (a) continuous 30×10^6 operations at 500 cps
          (b) intermittent 10,000 hours

TECHNICAL SPECIFICATION SHEET SCL-6316/3
LATCHING STATIC RELAY SPDT

1. Physical Requirements

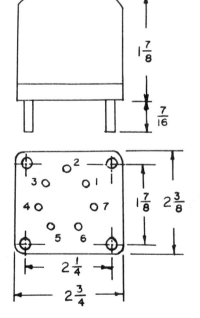

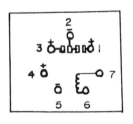

Dimensions in inches
Tolerance: ±1/16
Weight:
Terminals: Teflon imbedded
0.625-in. solder studs

2. Electrical Characteristics

  a. Input
    (1) Maximum actuating signal 1.92 volts at 10 ua
    (2) Minimum releasing signal 1.16 volts at 2.5 ua

(3) Overdrive protection (25 C) 10 volts

(4) Maximum electrical interference 150 mv

(5) Input waveforms X̲ step, X̲ sinusoidal, _____ spike

b. Contacts

(1) Rated resistive load 250 ma, 28 vdc

(2) Two contacts common on low side

(3) Maximum leakage 2.8 ua

(4) Saturation resistance at rated load 1.95 ohms

(5) Maximum operating speed 5 kc

(6) Maximum electrical interference 110 mv

c. External power

(1) Standby voltage 28 volts dc

(2) Maximum internal interference 650 mv

d. Other

(1) Ambient temperature -55 C to +85 C

(2) Life   (a) Continuous 30×10^6 operations at 500 cps

(b) Intermittent 10,000 hours.

4. Design of Signal and Control Static Relays

ROBERT LANGFELDER

Walter Kidde & Company, Inc.
Belleville, New Jersey

Mechanical relays have been widely used throughout the electrical industry for many years. Basically they are simple devices, and are capable of performing well when used under appropriate environmental conditions to perform appropriate functions. There are five conditions under which their performance or life may be unsatisfactory:

1. Requirement of fast response
2. Requirement of very long cycling life
3. Severe shock and vibration
4. Occurrence of contact contamination
5. Presence of contact arcing

All these possible shortcomings are due to the use of a mechanical contact. Any component with a moving part has certain inherent limitations which may be minimized, but never completely eliminated.

With the development of the transistor, and more recently the controlled rectifier, the possibility of producing relay-like action using only static components became quite feasible. Under Signal Corps Contracts No. DA36-039-SC78170 and DA36-039-SC85240, Walter Kidde & Company has developed, and is presently developing, static relay techniques and hardware.

For a device to be considered a true static relay, as distinguished from a static switch, isolation between the signal and power circuits must exist, and ON and OFF snap action must occur. Basically, in a static relay circuit, a semiconductor's impedance must be changed from a very high to a very low value when a certain signal level is reached, and changed back from this very low to the very high value when the signal level is then decreased to a somewhat lower value. This semiconductor shall be referred to as the "contact" in this chapter for ease of explanation.

41

The Contact

It is most reasonable to approach the overall design problem through a consideration of the possible contacts available. Figure 1 illustrates the appropriate rating ranges of the four semiconductor element types that seem most suitable at the present time. These ratings take into account both presently available characteristics and development types expected in the near future. Of these semiconductor contacts, only the controlled rectifier provides snap action without additional circuitry. At least two other contact ele-

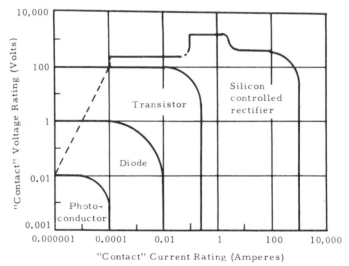

Fig. 1. Rating ranges of four semiconductor element types.

ments are possible. They are the magnetic amplifier and the vacuum tube. The former requires a-c power and will in general be larger and slower than a controlled rectifier circuit. The latter has comparatively short life, requires filament power, and can, of course, be replaced by a transistor in most cases.

Snap Action

Snap action can be provided by two alternate methods. The first method uses regenerative elements. This would include the controlled rectifier, the unijunction, the four-layer diode, and the newly developed tunnel diode. The second method uses non-regenerative elements connected in regenerative circuits such as the blocking oscillator, the Schmitt trigger, and the bistable multivibrator. Since isolation of the signal and power circuits is required, where a d-c signal is used and no regenerative element or circuit is present in the power side of a static relay, the only possible signal circuit is an oscillator made regenerative when some d-c level is reached. Where a regenerative element or circuit is present, the development of pulses of opposite polarity at two specific signal d-c levels is required.

Transistor Static Relays

The design of static relays using only transistor amplifiers requires the inclusion of an oscillator. Since a transformer is required for isolation, the simplest oscillator circuit requiring only a single transistor is the blocking oscillator.

Figure 2 illustrates a simple static transistor relay. Collector and base voltage are both provided by the input signal. To provide the low base voltage at a higher collector voltage, a Zener diode

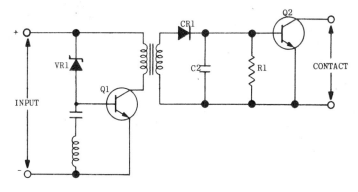

Fig. 2. Simple static relay.

is provided in series with the base. When the input level exceeds the Zener voltage by approximately 0.4 volt, the gain of transistor Q 1 increases until the loop gain exceeds unity and oscillations are produced. The oscillations are converted to dc in the secondary by half-wave rectification and drive transistor Q2 well into saturation. When the input voltage is reduced to the point where the loop gain is less than unity, oscillations cease and the transistor drive is removed. Half-wave rectification can be used without the capacitor since storage and fall time will maintain transistor Q2 in conduction during the intervals that diode CR1 is not conducting. The contact may pull out of saturation at low ambients using certain transistors, and the capacitor eliminates the need to select contact transistors. A static relay produced by Walter Kidde Co. with this design is rated at an output of 20 ma at 28 volts, an input of 3 ma at 10 volts, and an ambient temperature range of from - 40 C to + 100 C. Operation is satisfactory to about 20 kc.

Modification of this simple relay can be made to provide a contact rating of about 250 ma and to provide input overload voltage protection. These modifications are shown in Fig. 3. A resistor-Zener diode combination and R2 are added to the input circuit to provide overload protection, and an intermediate contact transistor is added to increase the output current rating. Capacitor C2 is connected to the end of R4 away from the emitter of Q2 to increase the RC time constant and reduce the size of the capacitor required. An auxiliary power supply to provide the collector voltage to Q1 would reduce the input current required to about 500 microamperes.

One requirement of Signal Corps Contract No. DA36-039-SC78170 was the development of a static relay with a contact rating of 250 ma at 28 volts requiring a signal power of less than 50 microwatts. To reduce the input power to this level, an additional stage of amplification and a separate source of collector voltage were required. Since isolation had to be maintained, the contact supply voltage was used as the input to a d-c to d-c converter whose output was used as the collector supply. The separate supply permitted the elimination of the Zener diode in series with the base. The final

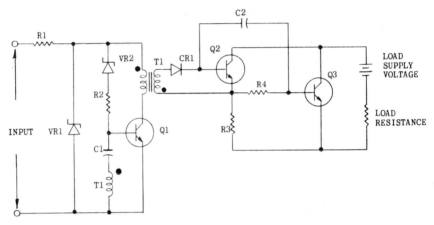

Fig. 3. Modified transistor relay.

units had a signal power requirement of under 4 microwatts at room temperature and a maximum of 23 microwatts at - 55 C. The final input circuit is shown in Fig. 4. The elimination of the Zener diode with the resulting reduction of signal voltage to about 0.7 volt at room temperature complicated the overload protection problem. Due to the voltage level, a Zener diode could not be used. The Zener diode voltage was replaced by the forward drop of diode CR1 in series with a voltage reduced from the collector supply voltage by means of a voltage divider (R2 and R3). To avoid applying even the voltage that could be developed across this combination directly to the Q1 and Q2 base-emitter junctions, resistors R4 and R5 were added. The result was that a signal voltage of over 15 volts could be applied over the entire temperature range without interfering with the operation of the final contact. The final d-c to d-c convertor used is shown in Fig. 5. Certain modifications of the standard

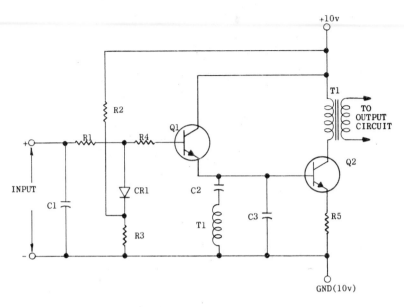

Fig. 4. Sensitive input circuit.

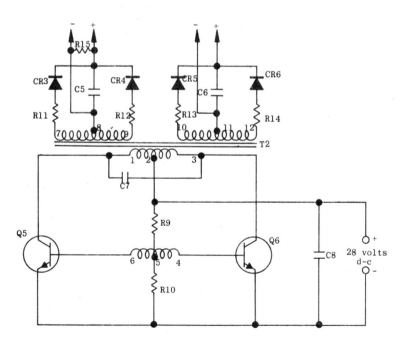

Fig. 5. DC to DC converter.

inverter circuit were required to keep the switching of the converter from interfering with the sensitive input circuit or from appearing in the 28-volt d-c power line, or the signal, or contact circuits. Capacitor C8 keeps the switching from significantly affecting the power line. Capacitor C7 increases the rise time of the square wave and reduces the higher frequency components. Resistors R11 to R14 were added, and fast recovery diodes were used for CR3 to CR6 to prevent the heavy circulating current which would otherwise occur in the transformer secondaries when inverter switching took place. This current must be minimized or the resulting field may couple into other circuits through stray capacitance or magnetic coupling.

Modifications of the SPST Static Transistor Relay

Four modifications of the basic sensitive relay were developed. The purpose of these modifications was to duplicate the functions of other than simple SPST relay types.

Figure 6 is a schematic of a polar relay. Essentially, this is simply two SPST relays whose inputs are connected with opposite polarity to the signal circuits. Both input circuits use the same converter secondary and the input diodes block the reverse signal polarity when the normal voltage is applied to the other input. In addition, these diodes prevent the secondary from being short-circuited through the common lines. Separate secondaries were used on the individual output circuits to permit either SPDT or DPST connections. Due to the differences in mechanical construction, it was found that resistors in series with the converter diodes were not required in this unit.

Figure 7 is a schematic of a latching polar relay. The latching function is performed by a bistable multivibrator. The blocking oscillators are used to switch the state of the multivibrator rather than to provide constant base current drive.

Figure 8 is a schematic of a DPST relay. Transistors Q1 to Q4 function as in the SPST relay. In addition, the emitter of Q3 is returned to the converter ground through CR9 and R8. When Q3 is conducting, the voltage across R8 cuts off Q5, and hence Q7. When the oscillator using transformer T2 is in a non-oscillatory state, the other oscillator is kept ON by means of the base voltage provided across R7 by the voltage divider action of R6 and R7.

Figure 9 is a schematic for the conversion of the original SPST relay output circuit to yield SPDT operation. With the oscillator OFF, transistors Q1 and Q3 are not conducting. The voltage appearing at the collector of Q3 is large enough to cause Zener diode VR1 to conduct and deliver base current to Q4, thus closing the normally closed contact. When the oscillator is activated, Q2 is saturated and the normally opened contact is closed. In addition,

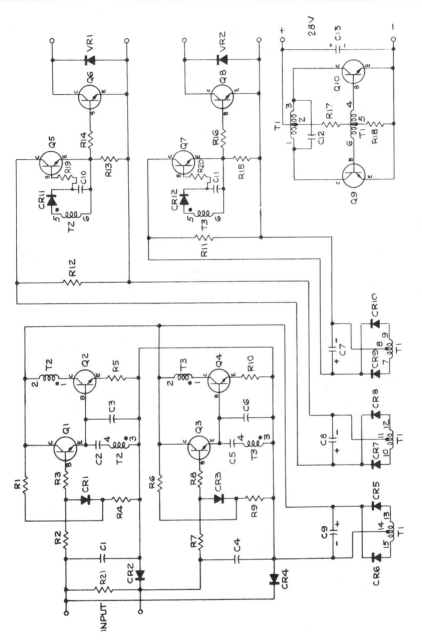

Fig. 6. Polar relay.

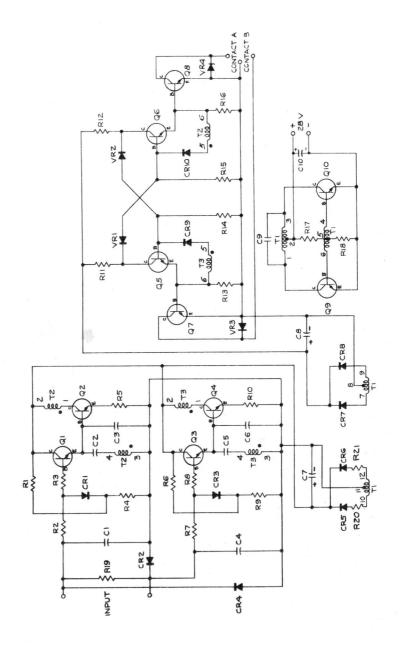

Fig. 7. Latching polar relay.

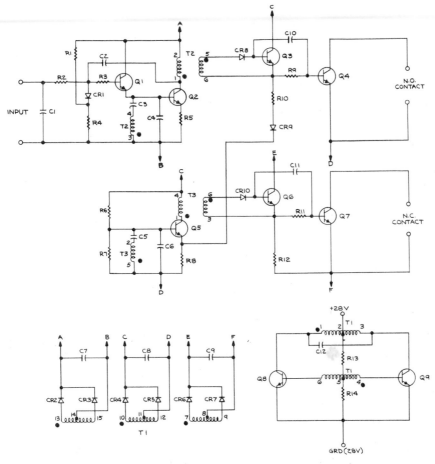

Fig. 8. DPST static relay.

when Q1 conducts, causing Q3 to conduct, the voltage at the collector of Q3 falls to a value low enough so that VR1 will block, and the base current of Q4 is reduced to zero, opening the normally closed contact.

Obviously, variations even of the basic SPST circuit are possible. Many other types of oscillators may be substituted for the blocking oscillator shown in these designs. Rectification of the oscillator's output may be performed on a full-wave rather than half-wave basis. The oscillator's pre-amplifier may be coupled to the oscillator in other circuit configurations, though the arrangement actually used was found to require the minimum input power of all combinations tested. Additional amplification may be added in the output circuit. Using only transistors, however, the basic design approach used seems the only possible arrangement to fully perform the functions required.

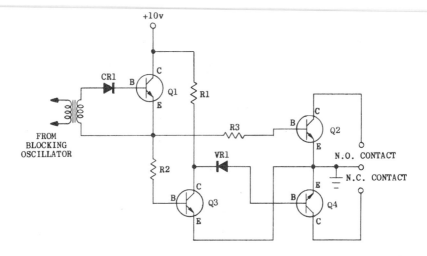

Fig. 9. Single throw to double throw conversion.

Controlled Rectifier Static Relays

The development of controlled rectifiers of various ratings and the verification of their reliability and good life capabilities within the last six to twelve months has established this type of element as an excellent choice for use as static relay contacts for all but very low current ratings. Their high gain and regenerative action are highly desirable properties when they are used as contacts. Their primary shortcoming lies in the difficulty of turnoff. Although controlled rectifiers of special design permit some turnoff by reversal of the signal on the gate (the Trigistor, Transwitch, Thyristor, etc), these are basically low current devices with low load current to turnoff gate current ratios. Actually, all controlled rectifiers can be assisted in their turnoff by this method at low load current levels. At high current levels, turnoff can only be accomplished by removing or reversing the applied cathode to anode voltage for a certain period of time.

One method of accomplishing turnoff is shown in Fig. 10. Pulses of opposite polarity will trigger the controlled rectifiers alternately. Turnoff is accomplished by capacitor C and inductor L, with diodes CR1 and CR2 assisting in improving turnoff characteristics. After the main controlled rectifier SCR-1 is triggered, the capacitor will become charged to line potential. When the auxiliary controlled rectifier SCR-2 is then triggered, the capacitor will discharge through the load. As its current increases, the current through SCR-1 will decrease until turnoff occurs at the point when the current falls below its holding current value. As the current due to L and C continues to increase further, the excess current will flow

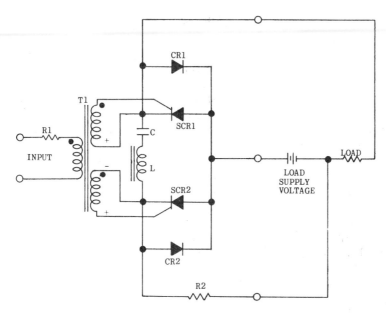

Fig. 10. Square-wave relay with controlled rectifiers.

through CR1, preventing a significant increase in load voltage at this point. When the current through L and C decreases again and can no longer maintain the load voltage above the load supply voltage, the normal voltage across SCR-1 starts to increase. If a long enough period of time has elapsed between the turnoff of SCR-1 and the reapplication of voltage, the controlled rectifier will stay OFF. Capacitor C will recharge to the full load supply voltage with opposite polarity preparing for the retriggering of SCR-1 and turnoff of SCR-2. Turnoff can be accomplished without the use of the inductor, but the value of capacitance required will be much larger. The inductor, in addition, permits a resonant reverse charging of the capacitor, causing rapid fall-off of load voltage to a low value before the slower decay occurs. The inductor also limits the peak diode current.

The circuit illustrated is for SPST operation. Resistor R2 can be made much larger than the load and the power loss is small. For SPDT operation, the second load can be substituted for R2. For multipole relays, the output circuit can be duplicated and extra transformer secondaries added.

For this type of output current and with d-c signals, circuits producing pulses of opposite polarity at certain signal levels are required. These pulses can be produced by regenerative elements such as unijunctions, controlled rectifiers, four-layer diodes, and tunnel diodes, or by regenerative circuits such as bistable multivibrators. Some of the possible circuits which require no auxiliary power supply are shown in Fig. 11. Some circuits using an auxiliary supply are shown in Fig. 12. The latter naturally require less signal power for operation.

One limitation to the use of controlled rectifiers as contacts is the maximum holding current. Below this current value, the contacts can be made to close, but cannot be held closed when the triggering pulse no longer exists. The minimum load current must exceed the maximum holding current that can occur for any unit at the minimum ambient temperature. It is for this reason that controlled rectifier contacts cannot be used for low current application.

Signal Relays

Mechanical relays are limited in their ability to pass very low load voltages due to the film which may form on their contacts. These low voltage, a-c dry circuit relays can be called "signal relays."

One objective of the present static relay development is the investigation of signal relays. There are at least three circuits to be studied. Figure 13 illustrates one circuit upon which some study has

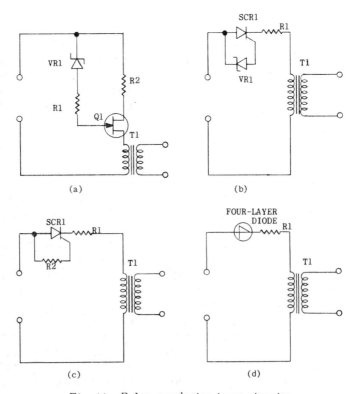

(a)   (b)

(c)   (d)

Fig. 11. Pulse-producing input circuits.

previously been done. A symmetrical transistor is used as the contact. When the blocking oscillator is activated, base drive is provided to produce saturation and low bilateral impedance, and apply the signal to the load with little attenuation. Diodes CR1 and CR2 provide a return path for the base current. If these diodes are perfectly balanced or series resistance is added to provide balance, no d-c insertion occurs in the load.

Using a germanium symmetrical transistor, operation with signals of 50 millivolts is quite good. When the blocking oscillator was deactivated, the signal was attenuated at the load by a factor of several hundred to one. Increased leakage occurred through the diode at high frequencies (above 5 kc) due to the recovery time of diodes CR1 and CR2.

The second approach is shown in Fig. 14. A photoconductor is used as the contact, and the control voltage is used to light or extinguish the lamp, changing the impedance of the photoconductor from about 10 megohms to approximately 100 ohms. This circuit is attractive due to its simplicity, and isolation is provided without the

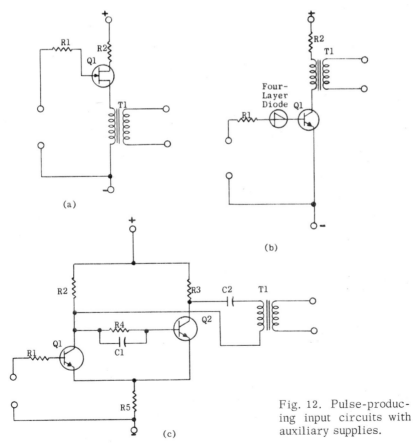

Fig. 12. Pulse-producing input circuits with auxiliary supplies.

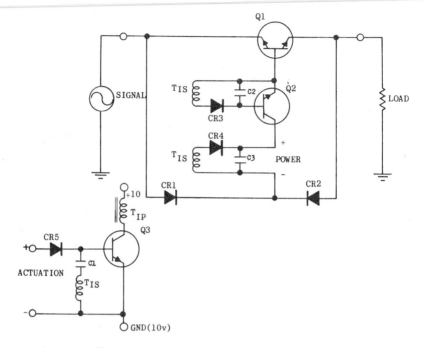

Fig. 13. Signal relay, symmetrical transistor circuit.

use of a transformer. Although the control power will be very high compared to the load signal power, this is not the fundamental problem, and amplification of the control power may be added when an auxiliary supply is provided.

The third circuit is shown in Fig. 15. This may not be the most practical approach due to the number of circuit components required, but it does illustrate the possibility of using biased diodes

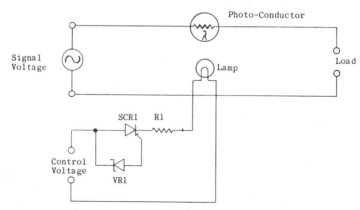

Fig. 14. Photoconductor signal relay.

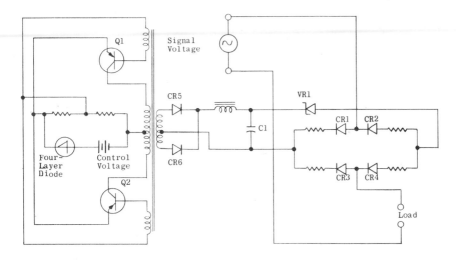

Fig. 15. Biased-diodes signal relay.

as contacts. When a diode is conducting forward current, it will pass a reverse current up to the value of the forward current. A d-c to d-c converter is used to provide isolation, and to transform from the control voltage to the voltage required by the diode. A four-layer diode provides snap action to energize the converter. When the control voltage is low, diodes CR1 to CR4 are not conducting forward current, and only negligible signal current can be passed. The forward paths through the diodes and capacitor C1 are blocked by the Zener diode. When the control voltage exceeds the switching voltage on the four-layer diode, the converter oscillates and passes forward current through the diodes. If this forward current is very high compared to the load current, the flow of load current will barely unbalance the diode bridge and produce a very small drop. This attenuation can be reduced almost without limit by increasing the forward current.

Summary

Static relays have reached the point of development where their feasibility cannot be questioned. No one, on the other hand, would advocate replacing all mechanical relays with static relays in all, or even most, cases. In applications where mechanical relays perform satisfactorily, they certainly should and will be maintained. Where marginal or unsatisfactory, they certainly should be replaced.

At present, static relays are, in general, larger than equivalent mechanical relays. However, the application of micromodule techniques should make static relays equal to or smaller than equivalent mechanical relays. In applications requiring multiple poles, the cost will probably always be substantially higher, and in most other cases, will be somewhat higher. This difference in cost will narrow as the price of semiconductors continues to decrease. The one-to-one comparison of size is not a fair one, however. Static relays can be built to do what mechanical relays can never do.

5. Non-Mechanical Relay

W. J. HILDEBRANDT*

Underwood Research and
Engineering Laboratory
Hartford, Connecticut

The conventional relay is a simple, easy-to-understand, easy-to-apply switching device. One of the major reasons for this is that the output has a very high resistive isolation from the input. It is instructive to consider a relay as consisting of two functional parts: (1) The switching element or contact itself and (2) the control element. Both the switching element and the control element will be assumed to be two-terminal devices which exhibit extremely small conductive coupling, although they may be coupled in other ways (mechanical, magnetic, etc). The control element is capable of changing the state of the switching element from open circuit to closed circuit or vice versa. To do so power must be supplied to the control element from an external source. Latching relays excepted, to hold the switching device in its non-normal state (closed for normally open contact) a maintained energization of the control element is required.

Specifications

On the basis of the foregoing assumptions the following broad specifications were formulated:
1. Conductive isolation of control and controlled circuits.
2. Elimination of moving parts.
3. Capability of multiple circuit control.
4. Power gain greater than one.
5. Control and switching elements capable of floating operation with respect to ground.
6. Speed of operation similar to conventional relays.
7. "Snap action" switching elements.

---

*Now with Connecticut Technical Corporation of Hartford, Conn.

8. Capable of being operated by direct or alternating current.
9. No extra power sources required.

Some Approaches to Realization

Magnetic Flux Control. One interesting possibility already used in a commercial relay involves the use of a transformer as the isolation means. (1) As another method, the magnetoresistance effect (2) can be applied so that the magnetic flux generated by the control element will cause a large change in resistance in the switching element. If the flux-controlled resistance itself cannot handle the demands of the external circuit, then this resistance can be made to control the base current of a transistor switch.

The bulk-rectifier effect (3) can be used in a magnetic flux controlled switch. In such a device the direction of the applied magnetic field determines the direction of "easy" current flow. By reversing the field one can change the resistance of the switch from a low value to a high value for a given direction of current flow.

Mechanical Control. The application of the mechanical strain sensitivity of certain resistance coatings is discussed fully later on.

Light Flux Control. Light flux can be used to control the switching element either by using a photoconductor or a photovoltaic junction device. The use of photoconductors with light flux control has been shown to exhibit the gain and isolation required for a relay-like device. (4) Light flux control of a p-v (photovoltaic) junction is the approach used in the relays described in this chapter.

The Basic Circuit

The basic circuit of this relay is shown in Fig. 1. Here the control element is the light source L, which is conductively isolated from the p-v cell C, that forms part of the switching element. The p-v cell when illuminated generates current capable of saturating the switch transistor T. When the light source is off, the base current of the transistor is essentially zero and this condition determines the "off" resistance of the switch. The relay is used to control direct current and polarity must be observed in making connections. Because of the isolation afforded by light control, such relay contacts may be placed in series-parallel arrangements with all the flexibility of conventional relays including locking or holding circuits, shunt down operation, etc (with the exceptions created by the unidirectional transistor switch used).

Components. Before going into the circuit operation more fully, some component data will be considered. The light source used in the experimental relays is a miniature incandescent lamp, a commercially available model of the lamp developed by the Diamond Ordnance Fuze Laboratories, Washington, D. C. (5) Since this lamp is small (approx. 1/8 inch long by 3/64 inch diameter) and its power dissipation low (approximately 50 milliwatts) one may position the p-v cells very close to the light source to obtain high illumination intensities. This lamp will provide full intensity about 5 milliseconds after voltage is applied. Although no life data are available it is believed this type of lamp is capable of providing a useful life of 10,000 hours "on" time.

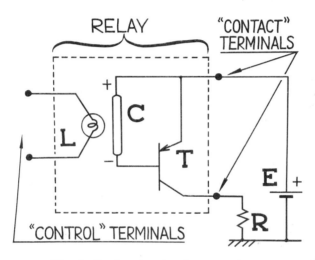

Fig. 1. Basic circuit of a non-mechanical relay.

The p-v cells used are the silicon junction type presently commercially available. No attempt was made to obtain selected high efficiency cells which will provide higher gains. The time response of the p-v cells is about 20 microseconds; the spectral response extends into the near infrared and provides a good match for the incandescent light source. Commercially available germanium transistors were used as the switches.

Physical construction of the experimental relays featured molding the p-v cells and the light source in a water-white styrene material as shown in Fig. 2. A separate lamp and p-v cell are also illustrated. No attempt at commercial packaging or miniaturization was made in the experimental models. To utilize as much of the lamp output as possible, the lamp is surrounded by p-v cells; the cells may each drive separate, isolated transistors to yield a multicontact relay, or they may be paralleled to provide high power gain to one transistor contact.

Circuit Performance. In the circuit shown in Fig. 1, a single

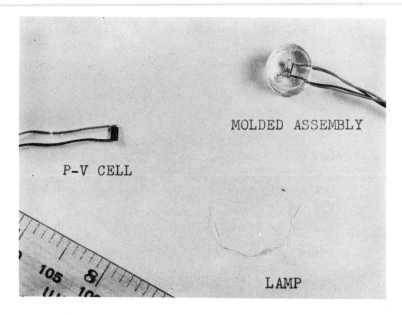

Fig. 2. Photovoltaic cell, lamp, and assembly (actual size) used in circuit described.

p-v cell with 30 milliwatts input to the lamp will saturate a Type 2N527 transistor and provide power gains of about 30. Figure **3** shows a circuit which has higher gain and may be used to control considerable power. Here the p-v cell generates the base current for transistor T-1, and T-1 provides a conductive path for the base current of transistor T-2. Although this arrangement is degenerative, it was chosen because of the requirement that the control and switching elements be capable of floating operation. In other words, no leads but the input leads and the output leads must

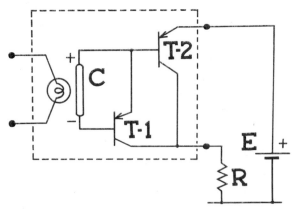

Fig. 3. Non-mechanical relay circuit with increased power gain.

leave the relay proper. The circuit in Fig. 3 has exhibited power gains in excess of 1000, controlling 40 watts to a 20-ohm load using about 30 milliwatts of control power. Under these conditions, the power loss when the relay is "on" is roughly 1-1/2 watts, while the power leakage to the load when "off" is about 5 milliwatts.

Turn-on time for these devices depends primarily on the light source and the external driving source impedance. Since the light source is an incandescent lamp, its resistance increases during turn-on. In one lamp used, the resistance changes from 5 ohms cold to 35 ohms hot. Because of this, the turn-on time can be as

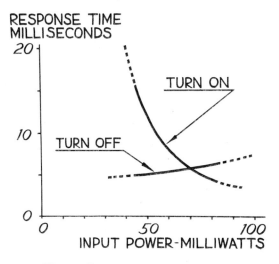

Fig. 4. Response time vs. input power for a non-mechanical relay driven from a medium impedance source.

much as five times longer with a high impedance driving source Figure 4 shows the variation of turn-on time with lamp power for a typical relay. In this case 15 watts is being controlled to a 27-ohm load. The driving source impedance is about 20 percent of the cold resistance of the lamp.

Effects of Feedback. The relays described so far have a draw-back in that they do not provide the positive " snap" action that usually characterizes conventional relay operation. To obtain such action, positive feedback may be applied as shown in Fig. 5a. A small portion of the output current is fed back through a second lamp which illuminates the p-v cell. Figure 5b shows the transfer characteristics with feedback and without. With the amount of feedback used, regeneration occurs at point A during turn-on. This is not satisfactory, but if more feedback is applied without means of limiting the lamp current, excessive lamp currents may be

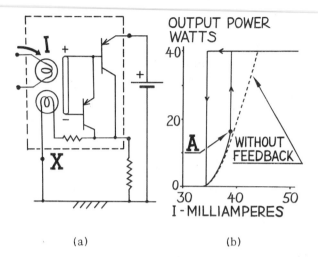

(a)

(b)

Fig. 5. Positive feedback connection to provide snap action (a), and
transfer characteristic (b) of circuit at left.

drawn and the relay will lock " on," and cannot be turned off by removing the input. One way of increasing the loop gain while retaining input control is described below.

Another problem with this approach is that a ground lead is
necessary (see point X in Fig. 5a). The ideal solution would involve no leads from the relay other than the input leads and the
output leads. If this requirement is maintained, then most of the
familiar " snap" action switching circuits become difficult to
apply.

A different approach involving feedback to the second lamp is
shown in Fig. 6. This circuit uses transistor T-3 to increase the

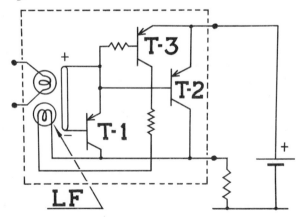

Fig. 6. More satisfactory means of
applying positive feedback.

gain in the feedback loop. Here T-3 will turn on the feedback lamp LF at very low load currents, causing the desired snap action. In one case where this circuit was used to control 40 watts to a 20-ohm load, the relay would snap to the " on" condition before the load power was more than 8 milliwatts.

Considering this circuit further, as soon as the switch transistor T-2 turns on, the effective supply voltage for T-3 is lowered to what amounts to the voltage drop across T-2, thereby cutting down the current to the feedback lamp considerably. Thus, the feedback lamp has most power fed to it when the system is in the neighborhood of the switching point.

Applicability. Since the input and output of these relays are isolated, the same circuit application freedom exists as for conventional relays. Generally, these relays may be controlled by ac or dc although the ones investigated switched only dc at the output. The relays are sufficiently fast operating to follow signals in the neighborhood of 100 cycles per second; thus for ac drive, a high driving frequency must be used or an integrating filter may be placed at the p-v cell output. Multicontact relays may be constructed, as explained earlier, by using several separate p-v cells each driving separate isolated contacts.

Two disadvantages of this relay are worthy of discussion. The first is the lamp inrush current. At the instant of turn-on, before the lamp heats up, the drive current can be six or seven times the steady state current if a low impedance driving source is used. The initial peak current will be limited somewhat by the lead inductance, and of course quite a bit by the source impedance.

Another disadvantage is the difficulty in producing a normally closed contact within the limitations set for this development. Several workable approaches were ruled out because of the requirement that no additional power sources be used. However, there may be possibilities here if the proper power sources are available, e.g., a thermoelectric junction may supply internal bias currents. (6) No results can be reported at this time.

Mechanical Control

Although a non-mechanical relay is under discussion, most relay circuit applications have use for mechanically operated switches, and a switch without sliding, rubbing, or impacting parts would be useful companion component for the non-mechanical relay. For this job, a strain-sensitive resistance was considered. Strain-sensitive resistance coatings of high gage factor have been investigated, and such a coating can be applied to a mechanically flexible input member. (7) Figure 7 shows a workable circuit approach, using the basic non-mechanical relay. A source of power is required for energizing the lamp, but it is completely isolated from the output circuit. Most of the lamps tested showed a practical illumination threshold at about half rated current, when the lamp resistance is roughly half its steady state "hot" resistance. Thus, the p-v cell and switch transistor will be "off" even though there is an idling current flowing in the lamp when the strain sensitive resistance is in its high resistance state.

Feedback can be added electrically as discussed previously, or mechanically, by making the mechanical structure snap acting for positive switching. Either normally open or normally closed con-

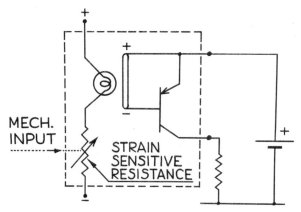

Fig. 7. Contactless mechanical switch.

tacts may be obtained by proper mechanical biasing of the strain producing member. A certain amount of preliminary work has been done on this concept, but no experimental results are available at this time.

Future Developments

The future of light controlled devices of this type looks very bright. The phenomenon of electroluminescense holds promise for long life light sources. (8, 9) Especially interesting is carrier injection electroluminescense which will produce light from direct or alternating current. Materials of the latter type have light producing response times of the order of 20 microseconds. (10)

Conclusion

A non-mechanical relay having input-output isolation, power gains of over 1000 and switching times of 5 milliseconds was studied. Feedback can be applied to obtain "snap" action and the relay contacts can be arranged in series-parallel networks similar to conventional relays. A means of mechanical control was proposed as a non-mechanical switch for application with systems using this relay. It is believed that practical devices with the simplicity and ease of application of conventional relays will result.

Acknowledgements

The author wishes to thank the Underwood Corporation for its permission to present this information, and Mr. A. F. Miller for his advice and help in molding the lamp assemblies.

REFERENCES

1. _____, Static Relay, Walter Kidde and Co. brochure, 1958.
2. _____, "Magneto Resistance— New Tool for Electrical Control Circuits," Electrical Manufacturing, Jan. 1959.
3. Herold, E. W., "Future Circuit Aspects of Solid State Phenomena," Proceedings of the IRE, Dec. 1957.
4. Loebner, E. E., "Opto-Electronic Devices and Networks," Proceedings of the IRE, Dec. 1955.
5. Belknap, D. J., and L. R. Crump, "Miniature Incandescent Indicator Lamps," Electronic Design, March 4, 1959.
6. Kelen, A., and P. Svedberg, "The Thermoelectric Transistor: A Possible Batteryless Amplifying Device," Applied Scientific Research, Sec. B, Vol. 6, No. 5, 1957.
7. Campbell, W. R., "Preliminary Investigation of the Strain Sensitivity of Conducting Films," Characteristics and Application of Resistance Strain Gages, National Bureau of Standards. Circular 528, 1954.
8. Destriau, G., and H. Ivey, "Electroluminescence and Related Topics," Proceedings of the IRE, Dec. 1955.
9. Henderson, S. T., "Electroluminescence," British Journal Applied Physics, Feb. 1958.
10. Wolff, G. A., R. A. Hebert, and J. D. Broder, "Recent Investigations on the Electroluminescence of Gallium Phosphide, "Proceedings International Colloquium Semiconductors and Phosphors, Garmisch, 1956.

6. Theoretical Considerations on Bistable Magnetic Amplifiers

J. J. SUOZZI

Bell Telephone Laboratories
Whippany, New Jersey

The bistable magnetic amplifier exhibits two stable states, one in which the gating and resetting cores are saturated resulting in full output, and the other in which the gating core is unsaturated while delivering current, resulting in low output. This chapter considers only that class of bistable magnetic amplifiers which result from applying excessive positive feedback to a basic full-wave self-saturating magnetic amplifier. (Bistable action resulting from inductive loads, or "ratcheting" due to core characteristics, will not be considered.)

The transient analysis of a bistable magnetic amplifier is complex because of its inherent nonlinear nature. In this chapter, a linear amplifier is treated first by using the conventional "approximate" approach. (1) The same amplifier is then analyzed graphically in a manner similar to that described by Finzi and Feth. (2)

Positive feedback is applied to obtain bistable action and the bistable amplifier is then treated by the same two methods of analysis. Some general comments on the effects of various types of feedback are given, and certain advantages and disadvantages mentioned.

Basic Full-Wave Magnetic Amplifier

The three basic full-wave self-saturating magnetic amplifiers are shown in Fig. 1. The bridge and center-tap circuits give full-wave d-c output while the doubler gives a-c output. The bridge circuit will be used to derive necessary expressions although es-

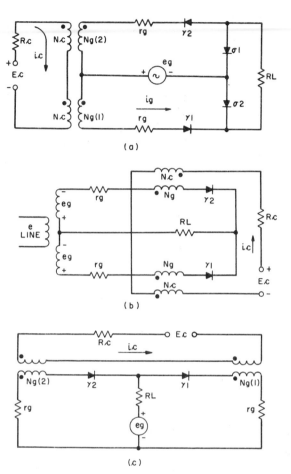

Fig. 1. Basic full-wave self-saturating magnetic amplifier circuits, (a) bridge, (b) center-tap, and (c) doubler.

sentially the same equations apply for the other two circuits. Only operation with relatively low control circuit constraint is considered.

The magnetic assumption used is the one developed in Reference 1, that is, that the half-cyclic average magnetomotive force F_p applied to the resetting core during its reset half cycle may be related to the preset flux φ_p which the core reaches at the end of its reset half cycle by a core "control" curve as shown in Fig. 2a. This information may be obtained from core tests such as described by Roberts or Hubbard. (3, 4) It may also be obtained from a measured transfer characteristic relating the half-cyclic average gross output voltage E to the half-cyclic average applied magnetomotive force, $N_c I_c$, as shown in Fig. 2b. If the core control curve is linearized as shown in Fig. 2a, its slope

$$K_\varphi = \frac{\varphi_p - \varphi_k}{F_p} = \frac{\Delta\varphi_p}{\Delta F_p}$$

This slope is easily related to the slope of the transfer characteristic over the positive Branch a, since for a self-saturating circuit, the gate circuit equation shows that $\Delta E = 2fN_g \Delta\varphi_p$. Hence, the slope of the transfer characteristic over the positive branch is simply $2fN_g K_\varphi$. Note that the transfer characteristic also has a negative Branch b, so-called because the slope is negative in that region.

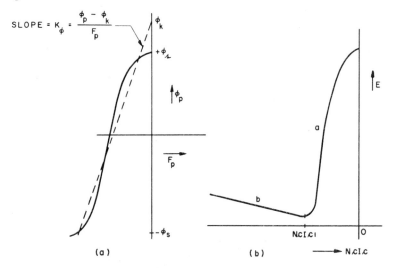

Fig. 2. (a) Core "control" curve and (b) transfer characteristic of basic bridge.

Consider the bridge circuit of Fig. 1a. On a positive half cycle of the applied gate voltage e_g, assuming that Core 1 is at some preset flux level φ_p as shown in Fig. 3a, the flux of Core 1 will rise toward positive saturation $+\varphi_s$. At the same time, the flux of Core 2 will recede from positive saturation to some new value of preset flux φ'_p. As soon as Core 1 reaches positive saturation, so-called "firing" occurs and practically all the gate voltage appears across the load R_L. In the next half cycle, the roles of Cores 1 and 2 reverse. Steady state is reached when φ'_p of a given half cycle equals φ_p of the previous half cycle. This type of operation occurs over the positive branch of the transfer characteristic, that is, for values of $N_c I_c$ greater than $N_c I_{c_1}$, as shown in Fig. 2b.

For values of $N_c I_c$ less than $N_c I_{c_1}$, assuming that Core 1 is at $-\varphi_s$ and Core 2 at some preset flux level φ_p as shown in Fig. 3b, on a positive half cycle of gate voltage e_g, the flux of Core 1 as-

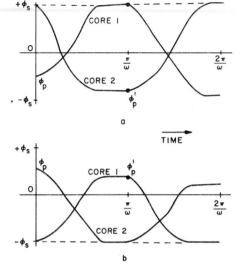

Fig. 3. Curves showing (a) flux vs. time for positive branch operation and (b) flux vs. time for negative branch operation.

cends toward a value φ'_p while the flux of Core 2 goes from φ_p to $-\varphi_s$. Note that Core 1 is unsaturated throughout this half cycle and that current is delivered to the load through the gate winding of this core. Hence, the gate current will simply be given by $N_g I_g = N_c I_c$ (neglecting the width of the hysteresis loop). Therefore, large values of control current I_c would be needed to obtain appreciable output.

Analysis of the Linear Amplifier (See Fig. 1a)

For operation over either branch of the transfer characteristic, the instantaneous control circuit equation for a step of d-c control voltage E_c applied is

$$E_c = i_c R_c + N_c (\dot{\varphi}_1 + \dot{\varphi}_2) \qquad (1)$$

where E_c is the applied d-c control voltage, i_c is the instantaneous control current, and $\dot{\varphi}_1$ and $\dot{\varphi}_2$ are the rates of change of flux in Cores 1 and 2 respectively. Equation 1 may be converted to a half-cyclic average relationship as follows:

$$\frac{\int_0^{\pi/\omega} E_c dt}{\pi/\omega} = \frac{R_c \int_0^{\pi/\omega} i_c dt}{\pi/\omega} + \frac{N_c \int_{\varphi_1 \text{ at } 0}^{\varphi_1 \text{ at } \pi/\omega} \frac{d\varphi_1}{dt} dt}{\pi/\omega}$$

$$+ \frac{N_c \int_{\varphi_2 \text{ at } 0}^{\varphi_2 \text{ at } \pi/\omega} \frac{d\varphi_2}{dt} dt}{\pi/\omega} \qquad (2)$$

For operation over the positive branch the value of φ_1 at time $t = 0$, referring to Fig. 3a is φ_p and at time $t = \pi/\omega$, $\varphi_1 = +\varphi_s$. The value of φ_2 at $t = 0$ is $+\varphi_s$ and at $t = \pi/\omega$ is φ_p or $\varphi_p + \Delta\varphi_p$. With this in mind, Equation 2 becomes

$$E_c = R_c I_c + \frac{N_c(\varphi_s - \varphi_p + \varphi_p + \Delta\varphi_p - \varphi_s)}{\pi/\omega} \tag{3}$$

where E_c is the half-cyclic average control voltage and I_c is the half-cyclic average control current.

If the transient is long compared to the time of a half cycle π/ω, Equation 3 may be written as

$$E_c = R_c I_c + N_c \frac{\Delta\varphi_p}{\Delta t} = R_c I_c + N_c \frac{d\varphi_p}{dt} \tag{4}$$

Equation 4 states that the increment of time Δt over which the preset flux change $\Delta\varphi_p$ occurs is π/ω, which time is small compared to the length of the transient. This equation is an approximate differential equation of the control circuit relating half-cyclic average quantities. For these reasons, this method of analysis has been termed the "slow transient" or "approximate" approach.

From the relationship shown in Fig. 2a, over the linear part of the positive branch

$$I_c = \frac{\varphi_p - \varphi_k}{K_\varphi N_c} \tag{5}$$

Substituting Equation 5 into 4 yields

$$E_c = \frac{\varphi_p - \varphi_k}{K_\varphi N_c/R_c} + N_c \frac{d\varphi_p}{dt} \tag{6}$$

Considering increments from some initial steady state only, for a step of E_c, the solution of Equation 6 becomes

$$\overline{\varphi}_p = K_\varphi N_c/R_c \, \overline{E}_c \, (1 - e^{-t/\tau_a}) \tag{7}$$

where

$$\tau_a = \frac{N_c^2}{R_c} K_\varphi \tag{8}$$

The gate circuit equation on an instantaneous basis is

$$e_g = R_g i_g + N_g \varphi_1 \tag{9}$$

where e_g is the instantaneous applied gate voltage, R_g is the total gate circuit resistance including the load resistance R_L, the winding resistance r_g, and the linearized forward resistances of the conducting rectifiers σ_1 and γ_1, and i_g is the instantaneous gate current. Integrating each term with respect to time and averaging over a half cycle yields

$$E_g = R_g I_g + 2f N_g(\varphi_s - \varphi_p) \tag{10}$$

or

$$E_g = E + 2f N_g(\varphi_s - \varphi_p) \tag{11}$$

where E_g is the half-cyclic average applied gate voltage, E is the half-cyclic average gross output voltage, φ_s is the saturation flux level, and φ_p is the preset flux level of the gating core at the beginning of the gate half cycle. (Note-Equation 11 holds for operation over the positive branch.) For constant gate voltate E_g, considering increments from some initial steady state only, the relationship between $\overline{\varphi_p}$ and $\overline{E}$ is obtained from Equation 11 as

$$2fN_g \,\overline{\varphi}_p = \overline{E} \tag{12}$$

Substituting Equation 12 into Equation 7 yields

$$\overline{E} = 2fN_g \, K_\varphi \, \frac{N_c}{R_c} \, \overline{E}_c \, (1 - e^{-t/\tau_a}) \tag{13}$$

Equation 13 shows that over the linear portion of the positive branch of the transfer characteristic for a linear amplifier, the output voltage changes exponentially as given by τ_a. Note that Equation 13 is of little use over the nonlinear portions of the transfer characteristic unless a new value of K_φ were defined at each point. The quantity $2fN_g \, K_\varphi \, \dfrac{N_c}{R_c}$ is the steady state voltage gain of the amplifier $K_E{}^*$.

The problem of analyzing the amplifier over the nonlinear portions of the transfer characteristic may be solved by graphical means. For a constant gate voltage E_g taking the derivative of each term in Equation 11 with respect to time yields

$$\frac{d\varphi_p}{dt} = \frac{1}{2fN_g} \frac{dE}{dt} \tag{14}$$

Substituting Equation 14 into Equation 4 gives

$$E_c = R_c I_c + \frac{1}{2f} \frac{N_c}{N_g} \frac{dE}{dt} \tag{15}$$

This equation applies over the entire positive branch of the transfer characteristic, that is, for values of $N_c I_c$ greater than $N_c I_{c_1}$ in Fig. 2b.

For operation over the negative branch, it is a simple matter to show that the control circuit equation remains the same as Equation 4. The gate circuit Equation 9 becomes for negative branch operations:

$$\frac{\displaystyle\int_0^{\pi/\omega} e_g dt}{\pi/\omega} = \frac{R_g \displaystyle\int_0^{\pi/\omega} i_g dt}{\pi/\omega} + \frac{N_g \displaystyle\int_{-\varphi_s}^{\varphi_p} d\varphi_1}{\pi/\omega} \tag{16}$$

or

$$E_g = E + 2fN_g(\varphi_p + \varphi_s) \tag{17}$$

where it is understood that the value of φ_p is that found at the end of the gating half cycle. (In Equation 11, φ_p is that value found at the end of the previous half cycle. This point is ambiguous in the

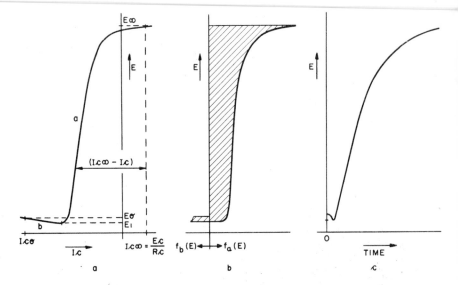

Fig. 4. Graphical solution for response time—linear case, (a) transfer characteristic, (b) plots of $f_a(E)$ and $f_b(E)$ vs. E, and (c) plot of response time vs. E.

approximate approach, but would be clarified in the "modular-difference equation" approach. (1). From Equation 17.

$$\frac{d\varphi_p}{dt} = -\frac{1}{2fN_g}\frac{dE}{dt} \tag{18}$$

Substituting Equation 18 into Equation 4 yields

$$E_c = R_c I_c - \frac{N_c}{2fN_g}\frac{dE}{dt} \tag{19}$$

which applies for the negative branch of the transfer characteristic. Using Equation 15 for the positive branch and Equation 19 for the negative branch, the response time of the linear amplifier may be solved for graphically.

Graphical Analysis of Response—Linear Case

Referring to Fig. 4a, assume that the amplifier is initially at a point dictated by I_{c_0}. A step of control voltage E_c is applied such that the steady state control current, $I_{c\infty} = \frac{E_c}{R_c}$. Over the Branch b, Equation 19 is valid and may be rewritten as

$$R_c(I_{c\infty} - I_c) = -\frac{1}{2f}\frac{N_c}{N_g}\frac{dE}{dt} \tag{20}$$

Since $I_c = f(E)$ as given by Fig. 4, separation of variables gives

$$dt = \frac{1}{2f}\frac{N_c}{N_g}\left(-\frac{1}{R_c(I_{c\infty} - I_c)}\right)dE \tag{21}$$

or

$$dt = \frac{1}{2f} \frac{N_c}{N_g} f_b(E) \, dE \qquad (22)$$

where $f_b(E) = - \dfrac{1}{R_c(I_{c\infty} - I_c)}$ and applies over Branch b only.

For operation over the positive branch, Equation 15 applies and becomes

$$R_c(I_{c\infty} - I_c) = + \frac{1}{2f} \frac{N_c}{N_g} \frac{dE}{dt} \qquad (23)$$

whence

$$dt = \frac{1}{2f} \frac{N_c}{N_g} \frac{1}{R_c(I_{c\infty} - I_c)} \, dE \qquad (24)$$

or

$$dt = \frac{1}{2f} \frac{N_c}{N_g} f_a(E) \, dE \qquad (25)$$

where $f_a(E) = \dfrac{1}{R_c(I_{c\infty} - I_c)}$ and applies over the positive branch only. Figure 4b shows plots of $f_b(E)$ and $f_a(E)$.

To solve for the time required for the amplifier to reach E_∞, the integral of Equations 22 and 25 is taken as follows

$$T_{total} = \frac{1}{2f} \frac{N_c}{N_g} \left[\int_{E_0}^{E_1} f_b(E) \, dE + \int_{E_1}^{E_\infty} f_a(E) \, dE \right] \qquad (26)$$

Equation 26 is integrated graphically as shown in Fig. 4c and the total time T is obtained.

The Bistable Magnetic Amplifier

When sufficient positive feedback is added to a linear amplifier, bistable operation can occur. Figure 5 shows a linear amplifier with a positive magnetic load current feedback added. The describing equations on a half-cyclic average basis using the "approximate" approach for operation over the positive branch are

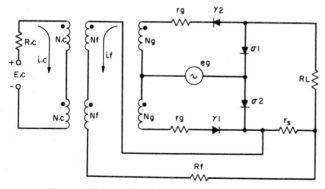

Fig. 5. Basic bridge circuit with positive magnetic load current feedback.

$$E_c = R_c I_c + N_c \frac{d\varphi_p}{dt} \qquad (27)$$

$$E_g = 2f N_g (\varphi_s - \varphi_p) + R_g I_g - r_s I_f \qquad (28)$$

$$r_s (I_g - I_f) = N_f \frac{d\varphi_p}{dt} + R_f I_f \qquad (29)$$

$$N_c I_c + N_f I_f = \frac{\varphi_p - \varphi_k}{K_\varphi} \qquad (30)$$

Solving Equations 28, 29, and 30 for I_c in terms of φ_p and substituting into Equation 27 yields

$$E_c + \beta(E_g - 2f N_g \varphi_s) = \frac{\varphi_p(1 - \beta K_E{}^*) - \varphi_k}{K_\varphi \, N_c/R_c} + N_c(1 + q) \frac{d\varphi_p}{dt} \qquad (31)$$

where

$$\beta = \frac{R_c}{N_c} \frac{N_f}{R_f} \frac{r_s}{R'_g} \qquad (31a)$$

$$R'_g = R_g + (R_L + r_g + r_\sigma + r_\gamma) \frac{r_s}{R_f} \qquad (31b)$$

$$R_g = R_L + r_g + r_\sigma + r_\gamma + r_s \qquad (31c)$$

$$q = \frac{N_f^2}{N_c^2} \frac{R_c}{R_f} \frac{R_g}{R'_g} \qquad (31d)$$

The solution of Equation 31 for a step of control voltage E_c, considering increments from some initial steady state, is

$$\overline{\varphi}_p = \frac{K_\varphi \dfrac{N_c}{R_c} \overline{E}_c}{1 - \beta K_E{}^*} (1 - e^{-t/\tau_a}) \qquad (32)$$

where

$$\tau_a = \frac{\dfrac{N_c^2}{R_c} K_\varphi (1 + q)}{1 - \beta K_E{}^*} \qquad (33)$$

The steady state gross output voltage is

$$\overline{E} = \frac{K_E{}^*}{1 - \beta K_E{}^*} \overline{E}_c \qquad (34)$$

If $\beta K_E{}^* > 1$, bistable action will occur. This criterion, of course, has assumed that the slope of the positive branch of the transfer characteristic is perfectly linear and equal to K_φ. In the practice, deviations occur. In any event, the linearized analysis over this region gives a starting point toward the design of a bistable circuit. Furthermore, approximate predictions as to the width of the bistable characteristic may be made using Equations 27 through 30. Another use of the linearized analysis is in predictions of the effects of different types of feedback on bistable operation.

Examination of the general control circuit Equation 31 shows that the factor β is an inverse function of the load resistance R_L. Therefore, changes of the load resistance will cause changes in the transient processes of the bistable circuit. When voltage feedback is applied, β is essentially independent of the load resistance, and changes of the load will have little effect on circuit operation.

The use of the linear analysis for predictions of response time is inadequate since the analysis holds over the linear unstable portion of the bistable characteristic AB shown in Fig. 6, and very little time is used in traversing this region, generally. Over this range AB, the process is one in which Equation 32 applies with

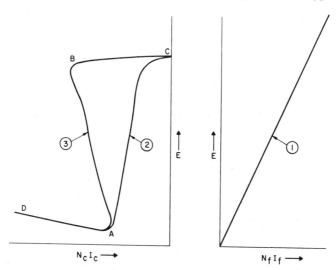

Fig. 6. Graphical determination of bistable transfer characteristic, (1) feedback ampere turns vs. E, (2) transfer characteristic (no feedback), and (3) bistable transfer characteristic.

$\beta K_E{}^* > 1$, and with τ_a negative. This implies that the term e^{-t/τ_a} increases without limit with time (until saturation is reached actually). To make reasonable predictions of response time for a bistable circuit, therefore, a graphical analysis similar to that of the linear case must be made. Given the linear transfer characteristic and the average feedback ampere turns as shown in Fig. 6, the bistable characteristic of Curve 3 can be drawn. This curve is a plot of half-cyclic average gross output voltage E versus half-cyclic average ampere turns N_cI_c for the bistable magnetic amplifier. Equation 15 still applies over the branch ABC, while Equation 19 applies over the branch AD.

The bistable Characteristic 3 now provides the needed relationship between I_c and E. Since it is nonlinear, a graphical plot of

$f_b(E)$ and $f_a(E)$ is necessary. This plot is shown in Fig. 7b. Graphical integration leads to the plot of response time vs E for the bistable circuit as shown in Fig. 7c by the same procedure as for the linear case.

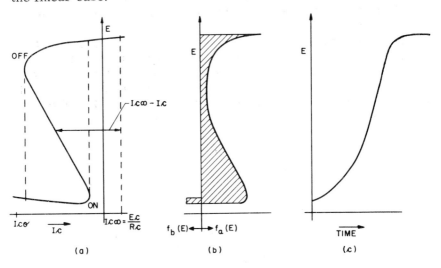

(a) (b) (c)

Fig. 7. Graphical solution for response time—bistable amplifier, (a) bistable transfer characteristic, (b) plots of $f_a(E)$ and $f_b(E)$ vs. E, and (c) plot of response time vs. E.

Discussion of Results

The bistable magnetic amplifier can be characterized by knowing the characteristics of the original stable amplifier from which it is derived. The maximum output attainable is the same as for the equivalent linear case. The magnitude of output in the "off" state is a function of the amount of positive feedback applied and the characteristics of the original amplifier before feedback.

The graphical analysis shows that the response time is shortened by increasing the actuating voltage, $E_c - I_c R_c = R_c(I_{c\infty} - I_c)$. Also implied in the above statement is the fact that faster response times may be obtained for bistable characteristics with sharper corners. This may be accomplished by increasing the positive feedback applied or by the use of frequency dependent elements. (5) On the other hand, an increase of actuating voltage implies an increase of input power. Also, an increase of positive feedback implies an increase of output in the "off" state.

The linear analysis is useful in establishing some basis of design for bistable operation and for predictions of the width of the resulting transfer characteristic. Some insight into the transient processes over the unstable branch AB (Fig. 6) of the bistable characteristic is also given by this approach, although the linearized analysis is restricted in predicting overall response time.

Conclusions

The bistable magnetic amplifier possesses certain unique advantages which makes it attractive in many applications. The amplifier affords galvanic isolation between various input signals, it may be controlled by very small direct voltages since its impedance level is very low, and it consists of transformer-like structures and diodes which are generally more reliable than semiconductor devices. In addition, the bistable magnetic amplifier may be biased to have memory if so desired. Its "on" and "off" points may be varied at will by simply changing the bias.

A limitation in certain applications may be its relatively slow response time. In addition, induced second harmonic voltages into the control circuit may be troublesome depending on the application. Whether or not to use a bistable magnetic amplifier as a static relay should be dictated by the particular requirements of a given system.

REFERENCES

1. Finzi, L. A. and J. J. Suozzi, "On Feedback in Magnetic Amplifiers - Part I - Single Feedbacks," A.I.E.E. Transactions, January 1959, pp. 1019-1030.
2. Finzi, L. A. and G. C. Feth, "Magnetic Amplifiers in Bistable Operation," A.I.E.E. Transactions, November 1955, pp. 592-598.
3. Roberts, R. W. "Magnetic Characteristics Pertinent to the Operation of Cores in Self-Saturating Magnetic Amplifiers," A.I.E.E. Transactions, January 1955, pp. 682-690.
4. Hubbard, R. M., "Magnetic Amplifier Analysis and Applications Using Block-Diagram Techniques," A.I.E.E. Transactions, November 1957, pp. 578-588.
5. Negnevitzkyi, I. B. and L. L. Samurina, "Transient Processes in Contactless Magnetic Relays," The Engineers Digest, April 1954, pp. 147-150.

7. *Bistable Magnetic Amplifier Switches for Signal Detection and Comparison*

WILLIAM LEVIDOW

Bell Telephone Laboratories
Whippany, New Jersey

A bistable magnetic amplifier is a static switching device capable of performing many of the functions of the electromechanical relay. Although its inherently greater reliability has been well publicized, the magnetic amplifier can also exhibit a greater flexibility, sensitivity, accuracy, and stability. These capabilities will be demonstrated by reference to the performance of several bistable magnetic amplifiers currently in production and use. Factors affecting the performance will be evaluated and a comparison made between the characteristics of the relay and the magnetic amplifier.

Sensitive Bistable Magnetic Amplifier

Shown outlined by dotted lines in Fig. 1 is a sensitive bistable magnetic amplifier used for signal detection and comparison and also for performing the logic operations of AND, OR, and MEMORY. Variations in core material and circuit connections can adapt this unit to meet a wide variety of requirements.

This type of circuit, whose output is full-wave rectified ac, requires a center-tapped transformer for the power source. The two control windings and the bias winding control the output voltage. Negative control or bias currents tend to turn the magnetic amplifier OFF, and positive currents tend to turn it ON.

Sufficient positive feedback results in a control characteristic of average load voltage vs. net control and bias ampere-turns as shown

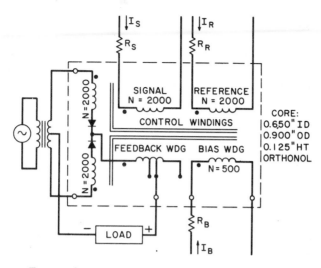

Fig. 1. Sensitive bistable magnetic amplifier.

in Fig. 2. With such a characteristic, this device may be used as a simple signal level detector, a comparator, an AND gate, an OR gate, or a MEMORY unit.

Figure 3a shows the basis of operation as a detector. To increase the sensitivity, the signal and reference windings are placed in series aiding. The negative bias current is then adjusted so that when the positive signal current increases to a predetermined level, Point "a" on the control characteristic is reached, and the magnetic amplifier snaps ON. When the signal is removed or is decreased to a level which brings the operating point to "b," the amplifier snaps OFF.

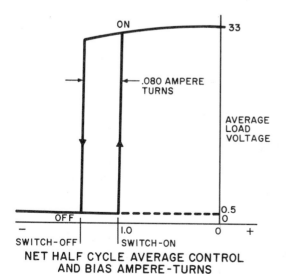

NET HALF CYCLE AVERAGE CONTROL AND BIAS AMPERE-TURNS

Fig. 2. Control characteristic of sensitive bistable magnetic amplifier.

The magnetic amplifier can also be used to monitor a diminishing signal by setting the bias at Point "c." The application of a sufficiently large negative signal will turn the magnetic amplifier OFF. Then when the signal diminishes to some predetermined level, bringing the net control to Point "a," the amplifier will snap ON.

Figure 3b indicates how the unit may be used as a comparator. Here the signal and reference windings are used independently. The unit is negatively biased to Point "a" and the reference is negatively applied to turn the magnetic amplifier OFF. When the applied posi-

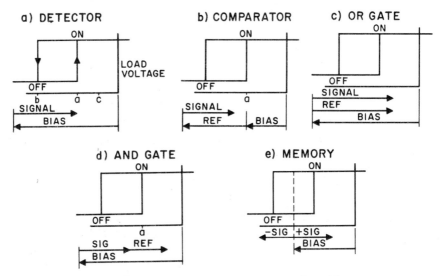

Fig. 3. Applications of the sensitive bistable magnetic amplifier.

tive signal equals the reference, Point "a" is reached and the magnetic amplifier switches ON. Here again the signal level to be monitored must be at least as large as the ON-OFF loop width in order that the unit switch ON and OFF with application and removal of the signal.

Operation as an OR gate is similar to that of the detector. The magnetic amplifier is negatively biased as shown in Fig. 3c so that a positive current applied to either the signal or reference winding is sufficient to switch the magnetic amplifier from OFF to ON.

Figure 3d indicates its operation as an AND gate. The unit is negatively biased so that the simultaneous application of the signal and reference currents is sufficient to drive the magnetic amplifier from the OFF to the ON state. It is necessary, of course, that neither control current acting alone be sufficient to accomplish this. This AND logic function may be extended to more inputs by the use of additional control windings or by performing the addition electrically external to the magnetic amplifier. As the number of inputs is increased, greater care must be exercised in the choice of bias and control currents to insure that normal variations in these quantities do not result in faulty operation.

MEMORY can be effected by biasing the magnetic amplifier at the center of the ON-OFF loop as shown in Fig. 3e. A positive pulse applied to either the signal or reference control winding will turn the magnetic amplifier ON and a negative pulse will turn it OFF. Successive pulses of the same polarity will produce no effect on the output.

From the above discussion of operation as a detector, comparator, and OR gate it is evident that in order for the magnetic amplifier to alternately switch ON and OFF with the application and removal of the signal, the signal ampere-turns must be at least as large as the ON-OFF loop width. Similarly, the loop width determines the minimum signal that may be used for operation as an AND gate or MEMORY. Although this ampere turn loop width is a function of the amount of feedback employed, there is a lower limit below which the switch-ON and switch-OFF points are not well defined and the transition between the ON and OFF states may be marked with intermediate steps. This minimum loop width, in terms of the change in signal current required to traverse the loop, is a measure of the magnetic amplifier's sensitivity.

From Fig. 2 which is a measured characteristic of a production unit having the design values given in Fig. 1, the sensitivity of such an amplifier is seen to be 0.080 ampere-turns. Using the full 4000 turns available, this reduces to a sensitivity of 20 microamperes. As applied, the signal circuit impedance was padded to 10,000 ohms which meant 4 microwatts of signal power was required to switch this unit.

The amplifier may be switched by a signal current smaller than indicated by the above sensitivity provided other means are available to switch the amplifier OFF before the sensing operation is repeated. This may be accomplished by a negative pulse on the bias or by momentarily disconnecting the a-c supply. The amplifier can then be biased just to the left of the switch-ON point so that a minute signal current will turn it ON.

This magnetic amplifier has a d-c output rating of 60 ma at 33 volts, or a power rating of approximately 2 watts. The exciting current results in an OFF output current of 1 ma, which with the rated load resistance produces a 0.5 volt d-c OFF output. This OFF voltage is proportional to the load resistance. It may be eliminated, if required, by load voltage biasing, as is described later.

Also shown in Fig. 2 are the ampere-turns required to bias this amplifier to the switch-ON point. This bias, as well as the feedback required for a given loop width, will vary from unit to unit due to variations in core characteristics. In sensitive devices such as described, in-process adjusting means such as taps on the bias or feedback winding and/or a rheostat in the bias circuit are used to compensate for these variations.

The feedback scheme used in Fig. 1 is termed load current magnetic feedback, since its ampere-turns are proportional to the load current and it combines magnetically with the other control and bias windings to reset the cores. Where dependence of the feedback, or loop width, upon the magnitude of the load current is a disadvantage, load voltage magnetic feedback may be used. In this case the feedback winding and a series resistor are placed directly across the load, the feedback then being proportional to the load voltage.

The accuracy of a bistable magnetic amplifier is determined by the variation in the switch-ON point or the loop width due to changes in environment, supply voltages, and load. In most magnetic amplifier applications the input signal, whether it be in the nature of a step or a gradually changing signal, is of such a magnitude that these small variations in the switch-ON point or the loop width are of little consequence. The digital inputs usually extend far to either side of the loop and the analog inputs are usually large enough to make a percent signal error negligible. However, where the application demands a sensitivity or accuracy far exceeding the capabilities of the conventional electromechanical relay, these variations must be considered.

It is obvious from Fig. 3b that a change in the bias current will change the signal required for switch-ON. From Fig. 2, a 1 percent increase in bias current produces a 0.01 ampere-turn increase in bias mmf. The signal mmf must compensate by the same ampere-turns, or 5 microamperes in 2000 turns. Hence a 1 percent increase in bias current will require a 5 microampere increase in the signal current for switching ON. The percentage signal error depends, of course, upon the magnitude of the signal. The change in bias current may be due to a change in the bias supply voltage or a change in the bias resistor due to temperature or aging. Where precision is required, use of a regulated voltage supply and premium resistors are indicated.

If the a-c supply voltage should increase, the flux excursion during gating in the OFF state will also increase. The greater this flux excursion the greater will be the flux reset required to just prevent saturation during the gating half cycle. Therefore, as the a-c supply voltage increases, the switch-ON point of Fig. 3b shifts to the left. Between the limits of ± 10 percent of rated voltage this shift is approximately linear with voltage and amounts to 0.004 ampere-turns of increased required reset for a 1 percent increase in voltage. This corresponds in Fig. 3b to a decrease in the switch-ON point of 2 microamperes in the 2000-turn signal winding.

When the bias is derived through a rectifier circuit from the same a-c voltage supplying the amplifier, it is interesting to note that the gate and bias voltages vary concurrently and in the same direction with variations in the supply voltage. From the previous discussion it is evident that the increase in required signal caused by an increased bias voltage will be partially offset by the decrease of required signal caused by the increased gate voltage. Hence, the resultant error will be the difference in error produced by each voltage increasing alone.

Since the flux excursion of the gating core in the OFF state is a function of the a-c supply frequency, the switch-ON point will also be affected by any variation in this frequency. A 1 percent increase in frequency will decrease the required reset by 0.001 ampere-turn or increase the required 2000-turn signal by 0.5 microampere.

The switching points of the magnetic amplifier are also affected by the operating temperature of the core. The commonly used core materials such as Orthonol and 4-79 Permalloy exhibit a decreasing saturation flux density and a decreasing coercive force as the core temperature is increased. This results in a shift to the right of the switch-ON point of Fig. 3b and also a decrease in the ON-OFF loop width. Over the temperature range of -30 C to +55 C, the shift in the ON point for this magnetic amplifier requires an increase in the 2000-turn control current of 4 microamperes for every 10 deg C increase in temperature. The corresponding decrease in loop width is 2 microamperes. The degree of shift depends upon the core geometry and material and is generally of little importance except in high sensitivity, high accuracy applications.

The character of the load also has an effect on the control characteristic. An inductive load will produce an effect contributing to the feedback and thereby widen the ON-OFF loop. This may be minimized by placing a diode across the load, the forward direction of the diode going from the minus to plus terminals of the load. This diode forms a shorting path at the end of the gating half cycle for the lagging current, which would otherwise pass through the gate and feedback windings. Use of this by-pass or shunt diode is also effective in preventing ON-OFF loop variations due to inductance changes from load to load.

The switching time of a given bistable magnetic amplifier may be reduced by increasing any of the following: The ON-OFF loop width, the degree of overdrive of the signal current above the switch-ON point, and the effective control circuit resistance.

The effect of control circuit resistance and the degree of overdrive on the switch-ON time of the magnetic amplifier of Fig. 1 is shown in Fig. 4 for two typical values of resistance. The abscissa is in terms of the steady state step of signal current through the 4000-turn control winding. The ON-OFF loop is 20 microamperes wide and the bias is adjusted at the switch-OFF point. Note that the switching time decreases as the control circuit resistance or the signal current step increases. Either of these measures will

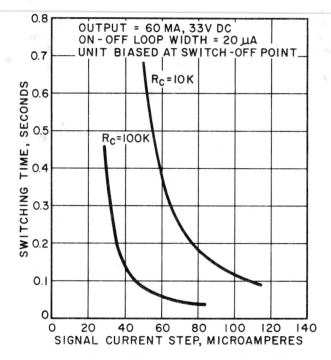

Fig. 4. Switch-ON time of sensitive bistable magnetic amplifier.

of course require a corresponding increase of signal voltage and power for switching.

This unit is packaged by casting the assembly in an epoxy resin. Its cast dimensions are 2-1/16 by 1-5/8 by 1-3/16 inches and it weighs 5 ounces. Where the unit is produced for a particular application, it is advantageous to include the associated components, such as the bias rheostat, the control winding resistors and the bypass diode, within the magnetic amplifier package. This allows the necessary adjustments to be made at the factory, provides a degree of protection for these components, and facilitates installation and replacement of the magnetic amplifier in the field.

Conversely, if only the winding and core assembly and the self-saturating diodes are packaged, the result is a highly versatile magnetic amplifier which can suit a variety of applications by adjustment of the external components.

25-KC Magnetic Amplifier

Another type bistable magnetic amplifier is a high speed switching unit developed for fault detection and corrective switching in a microwave radio relay system. Under normal operating conditions, the amplifier is in the ON condition and drives a set of double-throw mercury switches. Failure of the oscillator being monitored results in a diminishing signal current the amplifier switches OFF and the relays transfer the system to the alternate oscillator. Fast switching is of paramount importance to minimize the interruption of service during the transfer. The mercury relays also require a high ratio of ON to OFF output power.

Figure 5 is a schematic diagram of the magnetic amplifier showing the internal and external connections. The circuit is essentially that of a bridge rectifier with one gate winding of the amplifier in each of two legs of the bridge. Note that this bridge circuit eliminates the need for a center-tapped supply transformer. The load current is rectified a-c. Magnetic current feedback is employed to obtain the switching action.

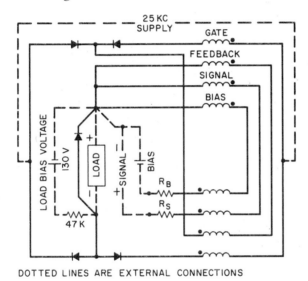

DOTTED LINES ARE EXTERNAL CONNECTIONS

Fig. 5. 25-kc magnetic amplifier.

To obtain a high switching power ratio, the residual OFF current is reduced by means of a load bias voltage. This voltage in combination with the 47,000-ohm resistor passes a current through the load equal and opposite to the exciting current. The OFF voltage is then reduced to zero or may even be made negative if desired. Hence the ON/OFF output power switching ratio can be made to approach infinity. The ON voltage is also reduced by this scheme, but this reduction is generally of little importance. A by-pass diode is placed across the relay load to minimize its inductive effect upon the switching characteristic.

Figure 6 shows the control characteristic for this magnetic amplifier. Normal control current is 2-ma output to a 4000-ohm load, or 1.6 watts. When the supply oscillator fails, the control current drops from 2 to zero ma. This drop may occur instantly or gradually, depending upon the nature of the oscillator failure. In any case, when the control current drops below 1.1 ma, the load current switches OFF to approximately zero value.

To obtain fast switching the magnetic amplifier is driven by a high frequency source. A 25-kc transistor core inverter was chosen for this purpose. This frequency is considerably higher than that generally used for magnetic amplifiers and care must be taken to

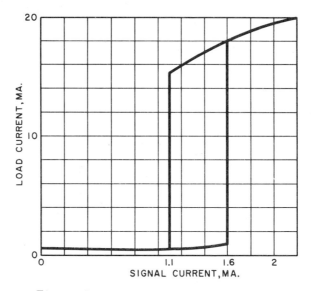

Fig. 6. Control characteristic of 25-kc magnetic amplifier.

minimize the effects of winding capacitance, which at this frequency become quite pronounced. Use of this high frequency carrier results in a switch-OFF time in the order of 1.5 milliseconds when the control current drops from 2 to zero ma. Output to input power ratio for switch ON-switch OFF operation is 32,000.

The physical size of this unit is 2-1/8 by 2-1/8 by 2-1/2 inches and it weighs approximately 0.7 lb when potted with sand asphalt.

Magnetic Amplifier With Memory

A magnetic amplifier designed to provide overload protection for a high voltage power supply is shown in Fig. 7. Six of these are used in the system to monitor each of six high voltage circuits in the supply. The unique feature of this device is that it not only operates a circuit breaker to de-energize the overloaded circuit, but also employs memory to indicate which of the six circuits is faulty.

The amplifier consists of two rectangular loop cores wound and connected in a center-tap, full-wave, self-saturating circuit. The by-pass diode and the control and bias resistances are included in the amplifier package. The load consists of a pilot light in parallel with a normally closed circuit breaker whose energizing coil is disconnected when its contacts open. The a-c input voltage is obtained from a 60-cycle, 70-volt secondary, center-tapped transformer.

Figure 8 shows the control characteristics in terms of the control ampere-turns, the device being biased at the point corresponding to zero control ampere-turns. Curve P is the control characteristic of the amplifier with the pilot light load and Curve C is the characteristic with the composite load of the pilot light and the circuit

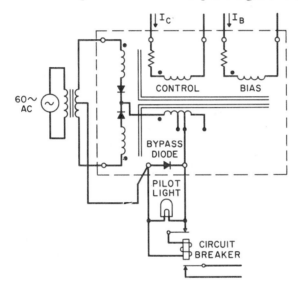

Fig. 7. Magnetic amplifier with memory.

breaker in parallel. A large amount of current feedback is employed to obtain a wide ON-OFF loop and thus provide substantial memory. Under normal operating conditions the control current is zero and the output of the amplifier is at Point A, or OFF. When an overload occurs in the monitored circuit, the control current increases, moving the output toward Point B. When Point B is reached, the amplifier switches ON, its output traversing the path B-C-D-E. Since the circuit breaker is set at 90 ma, it may operate at any point beyond C. The instant it triggers, the faulty circuit is disconnected, the control current drops to zero, and the output current wanders from its value on the composite curve to Point F on the pilot light characteristic. Although the current has dropped to approximately 30 ma, the amplifier is still ON and full voltage appears across the pilot light. Hence the memory function provides a visual indication of the faulty circuit even after the signal disappears. Although the magnetic amplifier is severely overloaded during the

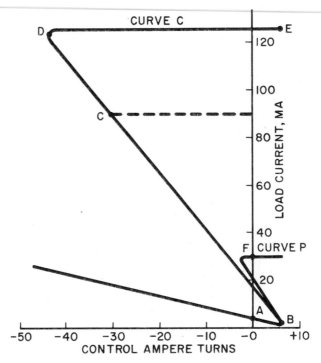

Fig. 8. Control characteristic of magnetic
amplifier with memory.

short interval between its switching ON and the circuit breaker's opening, the typically high thermal capacity of this type of magnetic device allows it to absorb the overload without damage.

The amplifier is reset to Point A by momentarily interrupting its a-c supply voltage. Adjustment of the bias enables the switching point to be set for control currents ranging from 1.5 to 60 ma.

All six magnetic amplifiers operate satisfactorily from the same supply transformer whose input has a ±1 percent voltage and ±5 percent frequency variation. Overall response of the monitoring circuit, the magnetic amplifier, and the circuit breaker is 10 cycles of the 60-cycle supply. The ambient temperature range is 10 C to 40 C. The physical size of the amplifier is 2-1/16 by 2-1/16 by 2-7/16 inches and it weighs 0.7 lb when potted with sand asphalt.

Comparison Between Relays and Bistable
Magnetic Amplifiers

A comparison between the performance of the conventional electromechanical relay and the bistable magnetic amplifier requires a consideration of their inherent differences. Whereas a relay operates to fully open or close a mechanical contact, a bistable magnetic amplifier operates to effectively insert a high inductive reactance into an a-c circuit. The relay may switch either a d-c or an a-c circuit while the magnetic amplifier can switch only an a-c circuit.

A magnetic amplifier is a single circuit control device. It cannot control several circuits as can a relay with multiple contacts. However, it may be controlled simultaneously from several electrically isolated inputs.

Being a static magnetic device, the magnetic amplifier exhibits a reliability and ruggedness approaching that of a similarly constructed transformer. Its life and operating characteristics are independent of the total number of switching operations. It can be mounted in any position. Its absence of moving contacts eliminates the troubles commonly associated with relays such as contact or bearing wear, contact bounce, contact sticking, chatter, and faulty switching during shock and vibration. The absence of an arc on switching OFF permits its use in an explosive atmosphere. It can be packaged in a plastic casting which protects the components from the damaging effects of moisture, fumes, and handling, and is generally designed to meet the requirements of Specification MIL-T-27A for shock and vibration.

Trends in the Art

Continued development of improved core materials and circuit techniques are certain to extend the role of the magnetic amplifier in signal detection and comparison applications. As an example, where a lower output power is sufficient the sensitivity of the amplifier of Fig. 1 has been increased several fold by the use of low coercive force-high gain materials such as Supermalloy or Supersquaremu. The lower saturation flux density of these materials approximately halves the maximum voltage output of this device, but the 4000-turn ON-OFF loop width is reduced from 20 microamperes to 1 microampere.

Operation at higher carrier frequencies to obtain fast switching is an area to be further explored. Here development of new core materials exhibiting a linear transfer curve at high frequencies will do much toward improving the response and the sensitivity.

Considerable interest has also been generated recently in the use of new geometric forms such as multiaperture cores, thin magnetic films, and magnetic strips. The work in these areas should lead to sharply reduced manufacturing costs and new capabilities and applications.

In an area once dominated by the mechanical relay, the magnetic amplifier has now become popular where response time demands are not too high and where a rugged, sensitive, maintenance-free static switch is desired.

8. Sensitive Triggered Oscillator-Controlled Switch Using Junction Transistors

RALPH A. BYRD

U. S. Naval Ordnance Laboratory
Silver Spring, Maryland

Current and voltage sensitivities ranging from several micro-amperes and 50 millivolts respectively up to any desired values are obtainable with a sensitive triggered oscillator-controlled switching circuit using junction transistors. The circuit is shown in Fig. 1 and some of the oscillator current and voltage waveforms are shown in Fig. 2.

Description of Circuit Behavior

Triggering-on Action (See Fig. 1). When the oscillator is not oscillating, a trigger current through the front-to-back paralleled Type 1N305 diodes determines the impedance of this diode combination. A positive input trigger current provides a bias which tends to cause the oscillator transistor to conduct. If the positive trigger current is sufficiently large, the corresponding resistance and bias voltage of the diode combination will cause the oscillator transistor to start to conduct (become active and amplify).

This initial collector current through the transformer primary winding induces a voltage in the feedback winding which causes the transistor to conduct even more. Thus, a cumulative effect is produced which causes the collector current to build up very rapidly through collector saturation to a value limited by the effective resistance in the collector circuit.* During this short time (or effective high frequency time interval) the transformer may be consid-

*The transistor reaches collector saturation when the collector junction becomes forward biased.

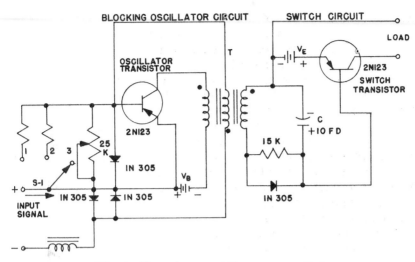

Fig. 1. Transistor oscillator-controlled
switching circuit.

ered as ideal except for the leakage inductance effects. The time
it takes for the current to reach this value is determined mainly
by the primary winding leakage inductance and the effective resistance of the collector circuit during this time interval. The maxi-

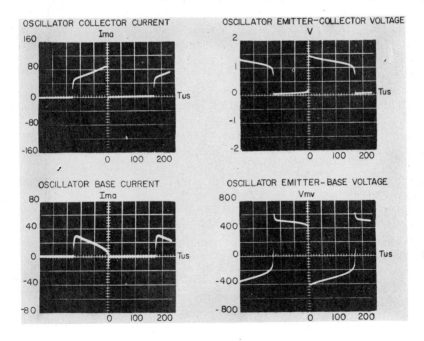

Fig. 2. Oscillator current and voltage waveforms.

mum rate of increase of collector current occurs during this period and, hence, the maximum feedback voltage causing conduction.

As the collector current increases very rapidly as explained, a transition point is reached where there is an abrupt reduction in the rate of increase of this current. The time required for the collector current to reach 90 percent of its value at this transition point is termed the turn-on time. The current during this time is defined to be the oscillator transistor turn-on current.

Oscillator Transistor Conduction Interval. At the end of the turn-on time the collector current continues to increase at a much slower rate to the value determined by the transistor base current amplification factor β and the base current. At this point the base current is determined primarily by the voltage induced in the feedback winding and the resistance in series with it. Since during this time this voltage decreases and the resistance in series with it increases (due to the non-linear resistance of the diodes), the base current decreases. At the instant the base current decreases below the value such that the collector current would be greater than the product of β and the base current, the collector current must decrease.

A decrease in collector current induces a voltage in the feedback winding which places a reverse bias on the emitter-base junction of the oscillator transistor preventing it from conducting. Because of the very short hole-storage and active-fall time of the transistor, this reverse bias causes the large collector current to stop flowing instantaneously (less than a microsecond) and induce an even greater negative bias in the feedback winding. Thus, the diode across the emitter-base junction of the oscillator transistor is needed to protect this junction.

Oscillator Transistor Non-Conduction Interval. The oscillator transistor remains biased off until the reverse bias voltage induced in the feedback winding decreases to zero. The time required for this is determined mainly by the inductance and resistance in the feedback winding loop. When the reverse bias decreases to zero, the cycle starts over again provided the necessary signal current is still present.

Sensitivity Control. The circuit may be adjusted for the correct trigger current for different transistors by means of the potentiometer across the oscillator transistor emitter-base junction. Negative temperature coefficient resistors across this same junction shunt part of the available current around the junction. Thus with the potentiometer, they determine the oscillator sensitivity and compensate for transistor characteristic variations with temperature. Switch S-1 permits selection of two predetermined sensitivities.

Sensitivities from several microamperes up to any desired current can be obtained. This corresponds to a voltage sensitivity range of from approximately 50 millivolts up to any desired volt-age.

Rectified Control Bias for Switching Transistor Operation. During the oscillator transistor conduction period, the impedance in the transformer load winding circuit is so high that this circuit has negligible effect on the oscillator collector circuit. The instant the oscillator transistor stops conducting, a voltage is induced in the transformer load winding which charges the condenser almost instantaneously through the forward impedance of the load circuit diode. This condenser voltage biases off the switch transistor. During oscillations the condenser remains charged to an approximately constant voltage because its discharge path time constant is very long compared to the time interval between charging pulses.

When oscillations stop, the condenser discharges to its steady stage voltage permitting good conduction in the transistor switch collector circuit. The switch transistor is biased on by the current from its battery supply.

Input Circuit Choke. The choke coil in series with the input signal blocks the oscillator transients from the signal source; but permits the passage of d-c and low frequency input signals.

Discussion and Results of Circuit Analysis

Oscillator Sensitivity. Maximum sensitivity exists when the oscillator transistor emitter-base junction has no shunt resistor. To determine the necessary condition for oscillations at maximum sensitivity, the load winding circuit is approximated by a battery V_A in series with the load winding, and the oscillator transistor is replaced by an equivalent small signal circuit (see Fig. 3). From

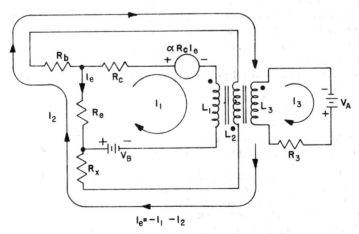

Fig. 3. Equivalent circuit for determining oscillator sensitivity.

this circuit's characteristic equation the condition necessary for oscillations was derived and is given by Equation 1.

$$R_x \leq \frac{R_3 \, [\alpha R_c - 2R_e] \, M_{12} - R_e \, [\alpha R_c - R_e] \, L_3}{R_3 L_1 + [R_e + R_c \, (1 - \alpha)] \, L_3}$$

$$- \frac{R_3 \, [R_e + R_c \, (1 - \alpha)] \, L_2}{R_3 L_1 + [R_e + R_c \, (1 - \alpha)] \, L_3} - R_e - R_b \quad (1)$$

R_x is the dynamic or small-signal resistance of the two front-to-back paralleled diodes.*

L_1, L_2, and L_3 are the transformer primary, feedback, and load winding inductances, respectively.

M_{12} is the transformer primary and feedback winding mutual inductance.

R_c, R_e, R_b, and α are the transistor parameters.

R_3 is the parallel diode resistor combination resistance in the load winding circuit.

Oscillator Turn-on Time. During the oscillator turn-on time, the oscillator transistor passes through the active region into the saturation region.† The oscillator transistor active region rise time is negligible compared to the total oscillator turn-on time. Thus, during the oscillator turn-on time, the transistor is approximated by an equivalent "T" resistance network consisting of resistors R_e, R_b, and R_k with the uncommon ends of R_e, R_b, and R_k corresponding to the emitter, base and collector leads, respectively (see Fig. 4). For large signal values such as exist in this portion of the cycle, R_e may be considered to be zero. A good approximation of R_k is the resistance in the oscillator transistor between the emitter and collector terminals when the transistor is in the saturated region. The transformer is considered an ideal transformer with leakage inductance, Le_1 and primary winding resistance R_a in series with the primary winding. The transformer feedback winding resistance is negligible compared to its series resistance R_x.

The oscillator transistor turn-on current causes a reverse bias to be developed across the parallel diode resistor combination in the load winding circuit, and this circuit is considered open during turn-on time. This is a valid approximation for values of the load winding circuit resistance considered here. Thus, the equivalent circuit (Fig. 4) is obtained, and the oscillator transistor collector

---

*In this chapter all circuit parameters except R_a, R_w, and C are a function of their current and voltage operating point. In most cases, average values for the parameters must be used for the particular region of the operating cycle under consideration.

†When the transistor is in the active region, the emitter-base junction diode is forward biased, and the collector-base junction is reversed biased. In the saturated region both junctions are forward biased.

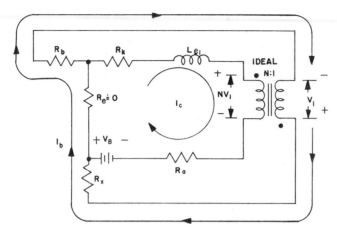

Fig. 4. Equivalent oscillator turn-on time circuit.

current I_c (t) during turn-on time was derived from it (Equation 2).

$$I_c(t) = \frac{V_B}{R_T} \left[1 - e^{\frac{-R_T}{Le_1} t} \right] \tag{2}$$

$$R_T = R_k + R_a + N_{12}^2 (R_x + R_b)$$

The oscillator turn-on time T_r is the time required for I_c (t) to reach 90 percent of its final value during the oscillator turn-on time (Equation 3).

$$T_r = \frac{2.3 \, Le_1}{R_k + R_a + N_{12}^2 (R_x + R_b)} \tag{3}$$

I_c (r), the oscillator transistor collector current at the end of this turn-on time, is given by Equation 4.

$$I_{cr} = \frac{0.9 \, V_B}{R_k + R_a + N_{12}^2 (R_x + R_b)} \tag{4}$$

N_{12} is the turns ratio of the transformer primary winding to the feedback winding.

Oscillator Transistor On-Time. During the oscillator transistor on-time, the transformer is considered as a perfect transformer with the equivalent primary winding resistance R_a inserted in series with the primary winding. The leakage inductance Le_1 is dropped now because the collector current varies only slowly. The same reasoning used in the oscillator turn-on time applies to the remainder of the circuit.

From an equivalent circuit thus obtained, expressions for the oscillator transistor collector current I_c (t) and base current $I_b(t)$ during the oscillator on-time were derived (Equations 5 and 6).

$$I_c(t) = \frac{V_B}{R_1} - V_B \left[\frac{1}{R_1} - \frac{L_2}{A} \right] e^{-\frac{R_1 R_2}{A} t} \tag{5}$$

$$R_1 = R_k + R_a$$

$$R_2 = R_x + R_b$$

$$A = R_2 L_1 + R_1 L_2$$

$$I_b(t) = V_B \frac{M_{12}}{A} e^{-\frac{R_1 R_2}{A} t} \tag{6}$$

Using these equations, the oscillator on-time T_c was derived by equating the product of β and the expression for $I_b(t)$ to the expression for $I_c(t)$ and solving for t. Equation 7 is the result.

$$T_c = \frac{A}{R_1 R_2} \ln \left[1 + \beta R_1 \frac{M_{12}}{A} - R_1 \frac{L_2}{A} \right] \tag{7}$$

Substituting this expression for T_c in place of t in the expressions for $I_c(t)$ and $I_b(t)$ for the oscillator on-time, the oscillator transistor collector current, $I_c(T_c)$, and base current, $I_b(T_c)$, at the end of the oscillator on-time were derived (Equations 8 and 9).

$$I_c(T_c) = \frac{V_B \beta M_{12}}{A + \beta R_1 M_{12} - R_1 L_2} \tag{8}$$

$$I_b(T_c) = \frac{V_B M_{12}}{A + \beta R_1 M_{12} - R_1 L_2} \tag{9}$$

Oscillator Transistor Off-Time During Oscillations. Transformer winding currents, which exist immediately after the oscillator transistor is biased off, were derived from the simplified circuit now indicated (Fig. 5). The collector junction of the oscillator transistor may be replaced by a switch, which opens at time t = 0, in series with the transistor resistance since the transistor's storage and fall times are negligible (less than a microsecond). The total resistance in series with the primary winding is R_1, and that in series with the feedback winding is R_2. In the load winding circuit the parallel diode resistor combination is replaced by a resistor R_3 and the emitter-base impedance of the switch transistor by a resistor R_y. The collector circuit of the transistor switch has negligible effect and is open. For this equivalent circuit (Fig. 5), the differential equation for

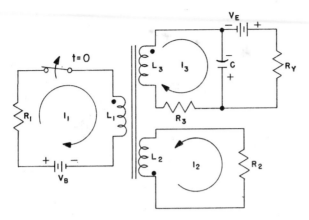

Fig. 5. Equivalent oscillator circuit for transition to off time.

the feedback winding loop was written. After substituting appropriate transformer inductance and mutual inductance relationships and integrating both sides of the equation from time t = 0- to time t = 0+, the relationship of the winding currents at t = 0- and t = 0+ was determined. The currents in the windings at t = 0+ derived from this relationship are given in Equations 10, 11, and 12.

$$I_1(0) + = 0 \tag{10}$$

$$I_2(0) + \doteq -\frac{N_{12}}{2} I_c(T_c) + \frac{1}{2} I_b(T_c) \tag{11}$$

$$I_3(0) + \doteq -\frac{N_{12}}{2N_{32}} I_c(T_c) + \frac{1}{2N_{32}} I_b(T_c) \tag{12}$$

It is assumed that the current in the load winding at time, t = 0- is zero. Obviously the currents in the primary and feedback windings, respectively, are $I_c(T_c)$ and $I_b(T_c)$ at time t = 0.

$I_1(0)+$, $I_2(0)+$, and $I_3(0)+$ are the currents in the primary, feedback, and load windings, respectively, at time t = 0+. N_{32} is the turns ratio of the transformer load winding to the feedback winding.

During oscillations while the oscillator transistor is in its off state, the condenser charges up to approximately the peak voltage developed across the transformer load winding which occurs at the instant the oscillator transistor stops conducting. For values of R_3 and C considered here, the condenser charges to its peak voltage in a very small portion of the available charging time, almost instantaneously.

As the condenser charges up to the applied transformer winding voltage, the diode in the charging path acts as a slowly opening switch, and the ampere turns of the load winding is transferred to

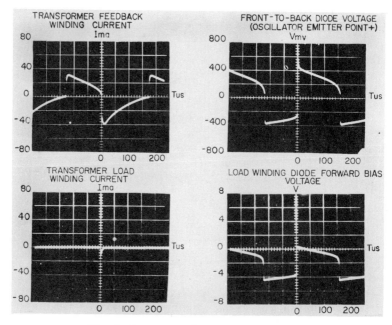

Fig. 6. Current and voltage wave forms.

the feedback winding as this diode switch is in the process of opening. Thus, the current in the feedback winding must increase initially to conserve the flux linkages before and after the diode switch opens. This effect is shown in Fig. 6. At the instant the diode switch completely opens, the current in the feedback winding reaches its peak. Thus current then decreases from this point to zero at a time rate determined mainly by the time constant of the feedback winding circuit with the primary and load windings open circuited.

Due to the very short condenser charging time compared to the oscillator transistor off-time during oscillations, the load winding may be considered as an open circuit for determining the feedback winding current during the off-time. This is a good approximation for reverse bias values of R_3 considered here.

Using these approximations Equations 13 and 14 were derived.

$$I_F(t) = [I_2(0) +]\, e^{-\dfrac{(R_x + R_z)\, t}{L_2}} \tag{13}$$

$$T_N = 2.3\, \dfrac{L_2}{R_x + R_z} \tag{14}$$

$I_F(t)$ is the feedback winding current during the oscillator transistor off-time. T_N is the time required for $I_F(t)$ to decrease to one tenth of its initial value, and is approximately equal to the transistor oscillator off-time during oscillations.

R_z is the forward resistance of the protective diode across the oscillator transistor emitter-base junction.

V_{LP}, the peak voltage developed across the load winding during the oscillator transistor off-time, occurs at the instant this off-time begins and is given by Equation 15.

$$V_{LP} = -N_{32}\,[I_2(0)+]\,[R_x + R_z] \tag{15}$$

From this an expression for V_c, the peak voltage developed across the condenser during the oscillator transistor off-time, was derived (Equation 16).

$$V_c = V_{LP} + R_3\,I_3(0) + \tag{16}$$

Since the time between charging pulses is very short during oscillations compared to the condenser discharge time constant, the condenser voltage remains approximately constant during oscillations. Thus, V_c is a good approximation of the average condenser voltage during oscillations and is of such a polarity as to bias the switch transistor off.

The reverse bias voltage V_{RB} applied to the emitter-base junction of the switch transistor is given by Equation 17.

$$V_{RB} = V_c - V_E \tag{17}$$

V_E is the switch transistor circuit battery voltage.

When the oscillator is not oscillating, the condenser steady state voltage is V_{FB} given by Equation 18.

$$V_{FB} = \frac{R_y}{R_y + R_3}\,V_E \tag{18}$$

R_y is the forward resistance of the switch transistor emitter-base junction. The load winding resistance is negligible compared to R_3.

Frequency of Oscillations. The frequency of oscillations, F is the reciprocal of the time required for a complete cycle and is given by Equation 19.

$$F \doteq \frac{1}{T_r + T_c + T_N} \doteq \frac{1}{T_c + T_N} \tag{19}$$

Switch Opening Delay. The delay time between the beginning of oscillations and a step input signal is determined by the time constant T_k, of the input circuit choke coil and oscillator input impedance. An equation for this delay time was derived from an input signal step voltage of amplitude 1.1 times the minimum amplitude required to trigger on the oscillator when it is set for maximum sensitivity. The oscillator input impedance for maximum sensitivity is R_x. An expression for T_k is given in Equation 20.

$$T_k = \frac{L_w}{R_x + R_w} \doteq \frac{L_w}{R_x} \tag{20}$$

L_w and R_w are the input choke coil inductance and resistance, respectively. R_w is usually negligible compared to R_x.

The delay between the beginning of oscillations and the described input signal is $2.3\ T_k$. Since the switch does not open until the end of the oscillator transistor conduction time during the first cycle of oscillation, the total delay time for opening of the switch T_{do} is given by Equation 21. Any required condenser charging time is negligible compared to the total delay time.

$$T_{do} \doteq 2.3\ T_k + T_r + T_c \doteq 2.3\ T_k + T_c \tag{21}$$

Switch Closure Delay. After oscillations stop, the condenser voltage is discharged from V_c to a value V_d equal to the difference between V_E and V_{FB}. At this point the switch is considered closed. V_d is expressed by Equation 22.

$$V_d = \frac{R_3}{R_y + R_3}\ V_E \tag{22}$$

T_{dc}, the time required for the condenser voltage to discharge from V_c to V_d, is determined mainly by the time constant of the condenser C and R_3. This is because the switch transistor is biased off by the condenser voltage during this time. V_x the condenser voltage during this time, is given by Equation 23.

$$V_x = V_c\ e^{-\frac{t}{R_3 C}} \tag{23}$$

T_{dc} (Equation 24) is the delay time between the removal of the signal and the switch closure.

$$T_{dc} = R_3 C\ \ln \left[\frac{(R_y + R_3)\ V_c}{R_3 V_E} \right] \tag{24}$$

Any additional time due to removal of the signal during part of the oscillation cycle is negligible compared to the condenser discharging time.

Frequency Switching Response. For parameters considered here, T_{dc} is greater than T_{do}, and for good switch operation for each cycle of a symmetrical input square wave signal, the maximum frequency of the signal is approximately the reciprocal of $2\ T_{dc}$.

Switch Impedance. The open switch resistance is greater than 1 megohm. The closed switch resistance is a function of the load resistance to be switched as shown in Fig. 7.

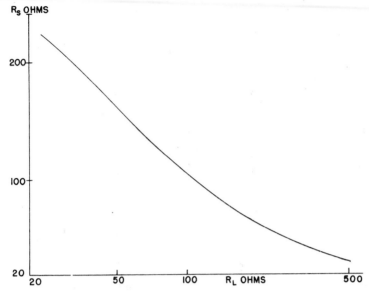

Fig. 7. Curve showing transistor switch resistance R_S vs. switched load resistance R_L.

Comparison of Experimental and Calculated Results. The calculated values compare favorably with the experimental results as
shown in the table. The close agreement in the results is good
evidence of the validity of the theoretical analysis and of the equations derived on the basis of the approximations made.

Conclusion

In conclusion certain advantages of this switching circuit will be
mentioned.
It can be made quite sensitive to current and voltage.
There are no contacts to become contaminated and cause a
change in switch resistance.
There are no moving parts to stick or wear due to friction.
There is essentially no d-c coupling between the input and
switching circuits.
This type device is not position-sensitive since there are no
moving parts which must be balanced.

Acknowledgments

The author gratefully acknowledges the assistance of Dr. E. A.
Schuchard, Mr. J. J. Moore, and Mr. J. J. DaRold. The author is
especially indebted to Mr. J. J. Moore and Mr. J. J. DaRold for
the experimental development of the basic circuit and information

Experimental and Calculated Results

Symbol	Experimental	Calculated	Units
R_x	5,350	5,042	ohms
T_r	5.0	4.92	μs
I_{cr}	50.5	47.3	ma
I_{br}	28.8	29.6	ma
T_c	130	129	μs
$I_c(T_c)$	94	91	ma
$I_b(T_c)$	4.0	3.64	ma
T_N	175	169	μs
$I_2(0)+$	-24	-26.6	ma
$I_3(0)+$	-10	-10.65	ma
V_{LP}	2.35	2.28	volts
V_c	2.0	1.94	volts
V_{RB}	1.3	1.2	volts
V_{FB}	0.146	0.144	volts
F	3.22	3.31	kc
T_k	*	0.505	ms
T_{do}	1.35	1.31	ms
T_{dc}	0.155	0.153	seconds
F_s†	3.3	3.4	cps

*The experimental value of T_k alone is not directly readily obtainable since it is dependent on R_x which is not constant.

†F_s is the maximum frequency of a symmetrical input square wave signal for which good switch operation can be assured during each cycle of the signal.

received from them concerning the experimental operation. Sincere gratitude is expressed to Dr. E. A. Schuchard for his advice, encouragement, and helpful criticism.

9. Solid-State Analog Switching Circuits

R. Z. FOWLER and E. W. SEYMOUR

Light Military Electronics Department
General Electric Company
Ithaca, New York

There are two general classes of applications in which transistors are currently in widespread use. Digital applications use the well-known switching properties of transistors and take advantage of the fact that a saturated transistor has a collector-to-emitter voltage drop that is negligible in comparison with the collector supply voltage. The typical digital circuit is quite content with a few tenths of a volt drop across the on-transistor. This is easily achieved and there is little to be gained by pushing it much lower. The second class of application is small signal amplification, in which the saturated condition is usually actively avoided and at best is considered a nuisance.

The bulk of today's electronic systems are implemented from these two classes of circuits. A third very useful mode of transistor operation, precision switching, has been largely ignored by many (perhaps most) transistor circuit designers. This is so in spite of the fact that adequate literature exists describing in detail the properties of the saturated transistor. A special case of precision switching has been rather widely described in the literature, namely, the use of transistors in low-level chopper circuits, and much has been written describing other uses of the technique.

The purpose of this chapter is to present transistor data showing d-c characteristics of saturated transistors, relate this to the theoretical models, and to describe several circuits which employ saturated transistors to accomplish the precision gating of analog signals.

Saturated Transistor Theory and Data

Ebers and Moll pointed out very early that the voltage drop from collector to emitter in a saturated transistor can be as low as a few millivolts. (1) They also pointed out that this drop is predictable and can be computed from easily measured small signal parameters. Consider a transistor with fixed base current, the polarity of which is arbitrarily defined in Fig. 1. The voltage drop from

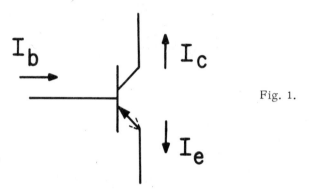

Fig. 1.

collector to emitter V_{CE} can be computed to a good degree of accuracy as follows:

$$V_{CE} = \frac{KT}{q} \ln \frac{\alpha_I \left[1 - \frac{I_c}{I_B} \left(\frac{1 - \alpha_N}{\alpha_N} \right) \right]}{1 + \frac{I_c}{I_B} (1 - \alpha_I)} \tag{1}$$

If we let $I_c = 0$, Equation 1 reduces to

$$V_{CE} = \frac{KT}{q} \ln \alpha_I \tag{2}$$

If, on the other hand, I_e is made zero, this is the equivalent of inverting the transistor so that

$$V_{CE} = \frac{KT}{q} \ln \alpha_N \tag{3}$$

Since α_N is normally closer to 1 than α_I, V_{CE} in the inverted condition is lower than that in the normal condition for zero current in the terminal serving as collector, for example:

$$\frac{kT}{q} = 0.026 \text{ volt at } 25 \text{ C}$$
$$\alpha_N = 0.95$$
$$\alpha_I = 0.85$$
$$V_{CE} \text{ normal} = 4.2 \text{ millivolts}$$
$$V_{CE} \text{ inverted} = 1.3 \text{ millivolts}$$

From Equation 1 we can also deduce that the effective dynamic resistance of a saturated transistor is reduced as I_B increases. This can be seen qualitatively by noting from the equations that for a given incremental change in I_c, the effect of this change on collector-to-emitter voltage is smaller as I_B increases. The curves of Figs. 2 through 9 show the measured saturated characteristics of several transistor types, and in a few cases calculated curves are given for comparison.

Circuit Applications

One case of precision switching which has been described rather

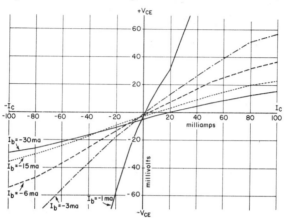

Fig. 2. Curves of voltage drop from collector to emitter (V_{CE}) vs. collector current (I_c) for various values of base current (I_b) for a Type 4JD1B4 transistor at 25 C.

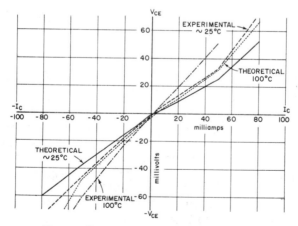

Fig. 3. Experimental and theoretical curves of V_{CE} vs. I_c at a constant value of I_b equal to 3 ma for Type 4JD1B4 transistor at 25 C and 100 C.

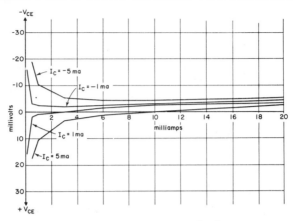

Fig. 4. Curves of V_{CE} vs. I_b for various values of I_c for Type 4JD1B4 at 70 C.

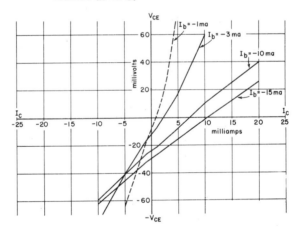

Fig. 5. Curves of V_{CE} vs. I_c for various values of I_b for Type 2N355 transistor at about 25 C.

widely is that of transistorized choppers. One form of a transistor chopper is shown in Fig. 10. The operation of this chopper may be understood by assuming that a squarewave is applied to the input transformer as a chopper control waveform. When the base of Q_2 is positive, the base of Q_1 will be driven negative since the two bases are driven from opposite ends of a tapped transformer winding. This will turn Q_1 on and will saturate it. Connecting the output directly to the e_1 input, at the same time Q_2 will be reverse-biased. Similarly, when the base of Q_2 is driven negative the base of Q_1 will be positive. Q_2 will thus be turned on and Q_1 will be reverse-biased. The output will now be connected to the input marked e_2. As this action is repeated, the output is switched re-

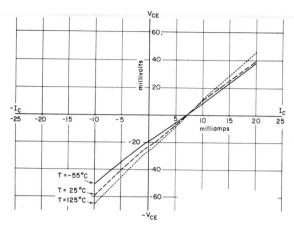

Fig. 6. Curves of V_{CE} vs. I_c at I_b equal to -10 ma for various temperatures for Type 2N355 transistor.

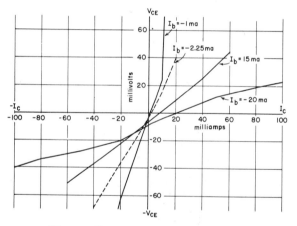

Fig. 7. Curves of V_{CE} vs. I_c for various values of I_b for Type 2N396 transistor at about 25 C.

peatedly from e_1 to e_2 and back. The control current is inserted into the transistor between the base and collector terminals rather than the base and emitter terminal. The total voltage drop across a transistor from collector to emitter is less when control current is applied between the base and collector than when it is applied between base and emitter. For this reason, transistors are generally found to be more desirable for chopper action when connected in the reverse direction.

Let us now consider the general case of a saturated transistor used as a series switch to control a signal. Figure 11 illustrates this. A signal generator is shown which generates a signal relative

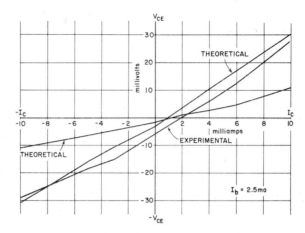

Fig. 8. Experimental and theoretical curves of V_{CE} vs. I_c for I_b equal to 2.5 ma for Type 2N396 transistor at about 25 C.

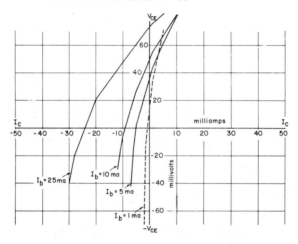

Fig. 9. Curves of V_{CE} vs. I_c for various values of I_b for Type 2N697 transistor at about 25 C.

to ground. Q_1 is in series with the output of the signal generator and drives a load R_L. If the transistor has zero base current, that is, is in the off condition, then no signal will appear across the load resistor except that small amount of signal caused by capacitance coupling and the very high series resistance of the off-transistor. On the other hand, if Q_1 is turned on, Q_1 will look like a very low series impedance. Furthermore, the transistor will present a low impedance regardless of the polarity of the signal. A qualitative way of looking at this is to consider Q_1 to be an emitter follower when the output from the signal generator is negative and

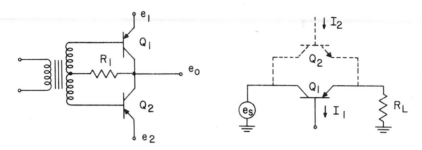

Fig. 10. Chopper.   Fig. 11. Simple bidirectional
                          gate.

consider it to be a grounded emitter stage when the output is positive. This requires a reversal of collector and emitter terminals
depending on the polarity of the signal. If the transistor is nearly
symmetrical, this occurs automatically and the transistor will be
a low impedance for either polarity. If the output impedance of the
signal generator is very low the current I_1 will not cause significant d-c displacement of the output voltage and will not cause a
pedestal to appear across R_L with the signal superimposed on the
pedestal. To eliminate this, bias current signal from the signal
source a second transistor of the opposite type Q_2 may be shunted
across Q_1. If the currents I_1 and I_2 are made equal there is no
unbalance current in the signal generator. Grossly unsymmetrical
transistors may be used while still maintaining accurate gating for
signals of either polarity. This technique also tends to cancel out
the small offset voltage which appears across the switching transistors and for a configuration of this type, the voltage offset may
be reduced well below 1 millivolt.

Figure 12 illustrates a six-diode gate. This gate is shown to
illustrate a switching circuit which may be significantly improved
by the use of transistors rather than diodes. In the six-diode gate
the gate is open when D_5 and D_6 are back biased. Under this condition current flows from +E through R_1 through D_1 D_2 in parallel
with D_3 D_4 and through R_2 to –E. Under this condition the signal
generator is connected to the output resistor by the series impedance D_3 D_1 in parallel with D_4 D_2. In the opposite state D_5

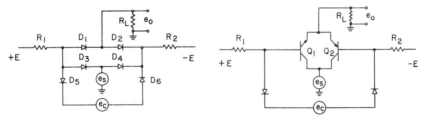

Fig. 12. A six-diode gate.   Fig. 13. Transistor equivalent
                                    of six-diode gate.

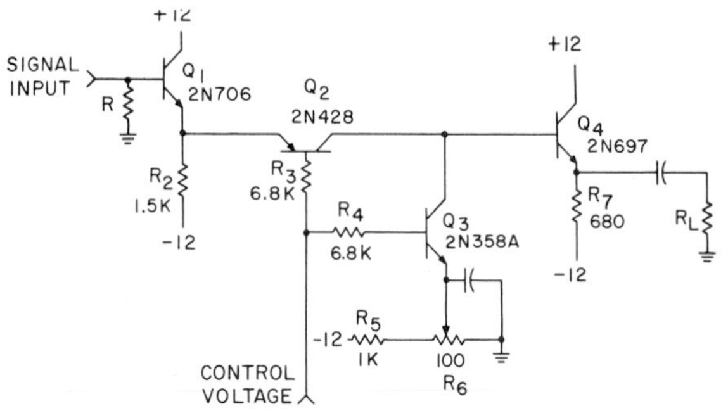

Fig. 14. Video gate.

conducts all of the current flowing in R_1 and D_6 conducts all of the current flowing in R_2. When this happens D_1, D_2, D_3, and D_4 carry no current and have a high impedance.

A gate which is almost identical with the six-diode gate is shown in Fig. 13. Here D_1, D_2, D_3, and D_4 have been replaced by two transistors Q_1 and Q_2. The control voltage is still supplied through diodes to control the current which flows in R_1 and R_2. A significant advantage of this gate is the fact that current gain occurs in Q_1 and Q_2. Furthermore, the voltage drop across Q_1 and Q_2 is in the millivolt region rather than being the difference between two rather large voltage drops as in the six-diode gate.

A practical gate for controlling video signals up to 5 volts in amplitude is shown in Fig. 14. The input signal is supplied to the base of Q_1 which is an emitter follower. The output of Q_1 is a very low impedance voltage source. Q_2 constitutes the series switch with Q_3 as a shunt switch across the output. Q_4 is a power amplifier which is capable of driving a 75-ohm load R_L. It may be observed that Q_2 is a PNP transistor with Q_3 a NPN. A common control voltage may therefore be used to control Q_2 and Q_3. When the input voltage is negative with respect to ground Q_2 is biased on and Q_3 is biased off. Under this condition the base of Q_4 is connected through a low series impedance to the emitter of Q_1. On the other hand, if the control voltage is positive with respect to ground Q_2 will be back-biased and Q_3 will be turned on. The base of Q_4 will under this condition be clamped to a-c ground and the emitter of Q_1 will look into a back-biased transistor. This circuit has been used to gate video pulses with approximately a 5-megacycle bandwidth. Linearity for pulses up to 5 volts is better than 0.5 percent. The pedestal offset which occurs when the gate is opened may be effectively reduced to zero by adjusting R_6. For all practical purposes the voltage gain of this circuit is unity.

In the case just described a low impedance source was available to drive the switch, thus making it unnecessary to worry about the control current which was inserted into the transistor base. In other applications, however, this control current may cause serious degradation in the circuit performance. If this is true the circuit illustrated in Fig. 15 may be used. The technique consists of switching a series transistor with current sources. A current source is inserted into the base of the switching transistor as well as the output circuit. These currents I_1 and I_2 are made precisely equal and thus do not load the input source.

This gate will accept a signal amplitude up to ± 10 volts. When the gate is enabled, the zero signal accuracy is about 2.5 millivolts. The unbalance current between the currents supplied by Q_4 and Q_5 is about 10 μamp for each percent mismatch between the 6.8 K resistors or the 33 K resistors. This unbalance current rep-

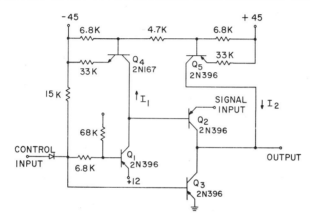

Fig. 15. Bipolar gate.

resents a d-c bias current that is pulled from the signal source. To enable the gate, the control input should be more positive than $+12$ volts. Q_1 and Q_3 are "off," current I_1 flows in the base of Q_2. To inhibit the gate, the control input is made more negative than ground level, turning Q_1 and Q_3 "on" (saturating them). I_1 is thus diverted to the collector of Q_1, and I_2 to the collector of Q_3, clamping the output to within a few millivolts of ground (depending on the base current of Q_3) and turning Q_2 "off." The impedance shunting the signal to ground when the gate is enabled is essentially 1/gc of Q_4 in parallel with 1/gc of Q_5 shunted by the collector capacity of Q_1, Q_3, Q_4, and Q_5, or about 300 kilohms and 40 $\mu\mu$f in this circuit. Switching time is of the order of 1 μsec and is influenced by the control input rise and fall times and to a certain extent by the impedance of the signal source. The positions of emitter and collector of Q_2 and Q_3 are essentially interchangeable so far as the gating action is concerned. They are shown as they are because of the voltage ratings of the transistors. It will be noted that the mismatch between I_1 and I_2 is independent of power supply variations.

If it is desired to have a common load for several inputs the circuit shown in Fig. 16 may be used. This circuit is essentially

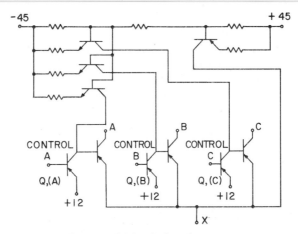

Fig. 16. Multiple bipolar gate.

the same as the circuit shown in Fig. 15 with the exception that extra inputs B and C have been added. Point X is the output for normal operation. However, Point X may be used as the input with Points A, B, and C used as outputs. In this case, the common source would be multiplexed between different loads.

To connect Point A to Point X, the control input at the base of Q_1 (A) should be more positive than the emitter (in this case $+12$ volts) turning Q_1 (A) off, and all other control inputs should be negative with respect to $+12$, turning Q_1 (B), Q_1 (C) etc, "on." The operation of this circuit is identical to that in the last example and similar signal levels and accuracy can be attained.

Another use for a saturated transistor as a switch is illustrated in Fig. 17. In this case it is desired to convert the input signal to a precise output voltage. In this case, two transistors Q_1 and Q_2 are used to switch the output alternately from ground to the reference voltage. A circuit shown here has been used very successfully as part of a digital-to-analog converter. One of these circuits is re-

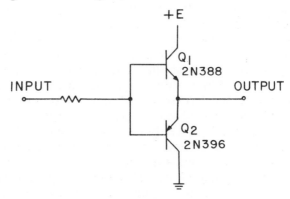

Fig. 17. Precision clamp.

quired per digit. The outputs are all combined in a resistor matrix. When the input is positive, transistor Q_1 is saturated. It is desirable to drive the input sufficiently positive to supply a base current to Q_1 on the order of several milliamperes, even though the output may be less than 1 ma, as was the case in our application. The same holds true when the input is driven negative to turn Q_2 on. Under these conditions most of the current flows between base and

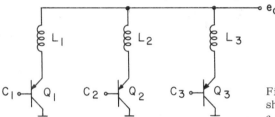

Fig. 18. Circuit for time-sharing a read amplifier for a magnetic drum.

collector rather than between base and emitter. As described previously, this mode of operation gives the lowest offset voltage in the transistor with the transistor types shown in the figure. It is possible to build digital-to-analog converters with better than 0.1 percent accuracy without any matching of transistors whatsoever.

Figure 18 shows an application in which it was desired to time-share a read amplifier for a magnetic drum. To do this, all of the outputs from the heads labeled L_1, L_2, and L_3 were connected together. The other end of the head windings were tied respectively to Q_1, Q_2, and Q_3. At any one time only one of these transistors is turned on. This technique has been used quite successfully to time-share magnetic drum read heads for digital applications up to 150 kc. And we believe higher frequenceis are achievable.

Conclusions

From the circuits just described it may be seen that it is possible to employ saturated transistors in such a manner that they closely approximate the performance of a mechanical switch in terms of series impedance both closed and opened while retaining the advantages of electronic switches such as high speed and freedom from mechanical movement. These circuits were not intended to be a complete listing of all of the ways in which saturated transistors can be applied. They have been shown merely to indicate the large range of possibilities which exist for using these transistors to achieve excellent.switching results. The gating circuits shown have series impedances in the order of a few ohms when closed and hundreds of kilo ohms when open. Furthermore, it has been shown that it is possible to design these circuits so that the switch itself does not significantly load the driving source.

BIBLIOGRAPHY

1. Ebers, J. J., and J. L. Moll, "Large Signal Behavior of Junction Transistors," Proceedings of IRE, Vol. 42, Dec. 1954, pp. 1761-72.
2. Giorgis, J., Application of Silicon Transistors in High Impedance Choppers, General Electric TIS 58APS115.
3. Cook, W. A., and P. L. Bargeillini, Solid State Circuit Symposium, Philadelphia, Pennsylvania, Feb. 1957.

10. UHF Automatic Direction Finder Antenna Chopper Using Silicon Diodes

A. A. DARGIS

Collins Radio Company
Cedar Rapids, Iowa

During the summer of 1959, Richard D. Baertsch and the writer investigated the possibility of replacing the mechanical chopper used in Collins AS-909/ARA-48 ADF Antenna with an electronic equivalent. As a result of this investigation an alternative was developed which uses high-frequency silicon diodes. This chapter describes the design work and the experiences encountered during the subsequent manufacture of the item.

AS-909/ARA-48 ADF Antenna Theory

A brief mention of the ADF antenna theory should be helpful in understanding the chopper requirements. When connected as shown in Fig. 1, the ADF antenna is directional and its field pattern resembles a cardioid. If the antenna terminations to ground and the receiver are reversed, a new image cardioid pattern will result with directivity differing from the first by 180 degrees. In the ADF antenna these terminals are continuously interchanged at a rate of 100 times per second. Thus, a signal coming from direction X1, as shown in Fig. 2a, will look stronger during the half cycle in which the antenna is connected to give cardioid pattern A, weaker during the next half cycle with the antenna connected to give cardioid B. (Compare the length of vectors A1 and B1.) This switching thus causes modulation of the received r-f signal. Figure 2b shows how

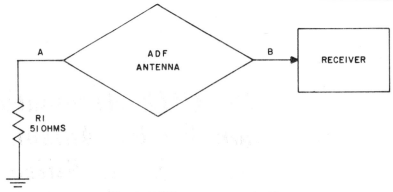

Fig. 1. ADF antenna terminations.

the modulation phase and amplitude will differ depending on the direction of the signal source. The modulated signal is detected, amplified, and used to rotate the ADF antenna until a point of zero modulation amplitude is reached. Then the rotation stops, and an accurate indication of the bearing of the received signal is obtained. The switching which continuously interchanges the antenna terminals is performed by a chopper which is expected to cause little signal attenuation due to insertion loss. In addition, good VSWR symmetry in both chopper positions is required to prevent undesirable error modulation at null. On the other hand, this chopper does not require switching isolation exceeding 20 db.

Mechanical Chopper

To understand the design requirements for the diode chopper, it is best to start by examining the unit which it replaced. The me-

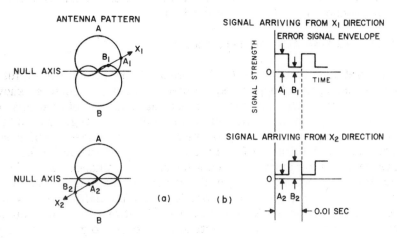

Fig. 2. Vector representation of ADF antenna modulation of a received signal.

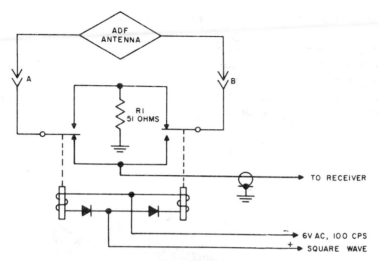

Fig. 3. Mechanical chopper schematic diagram
with ADF antenna connected.

chanical chopper whose schematic diagram appears in Fig. 3, is
activated by a 6.3-volt, 100-cps square-wave voltage. The two
diodes rectify this voltage, and the resultant current activates first
one side of the switch and then the other at the rate of 100 cycles
per second. This action alternately interchanges the ADF antenna
feed to the receiver and its 51-ohm characteristic impedance
termination.

Table 1 outlines the major specifications of the mechanical
chopper.

Diode Chopper Compared With the Mechanical Chopper

The diode chopper design requirements include complete electrical and mechanical interchangeability with the mechanical chopper whose major specifications are outlined above. The diode
chopper shown in Fig. 4 meets these requirements quite closely.
An exception is the VSWR specification which sometimes is ex-

Table I. Mechanical Chopper Specifications

Driving Voltage	6.3 Vrms, 100 cps square wave
Current	120 ma
VSWR	1.7:1 max over 225-400-mc frequency range
Ratio of VSWR's	1.1:1 max
Contact Rating	0.1 Vrms at 225-400 mc.
Temperature	-55 C to +100 C and 10 minutes at +125 C
Altitude	70,000 feet
Vibration	10 G's from 44-1000 cps

ceeded slightly in a narrow frequency band. This, however, does not appear to affect the performance of the ADF during field tests. On the other hand, the diode chopper has several important assets, one being its ability to operate under severe vibration. It withstands 75-g vibration in all three planes throughout the 44 to 1000-cps range. Two other significant advantages are the absence of contact bounce and negligible phase shift.*

Fig. 4. Assembled diode chopper.

Figure 5 shows the schematic diagram of the chopper. With the polarities indicated, CR1 and CR3 are biased in the forward direction. These two diodes will conduct direct current presenting a low (approximately 10-ohm) bilateral impedance to the r-f current. At the same time CR2 and CR4 are reverse biased and offer an impedance of several hundred ohms to the flow of r-f current. In this fashion the ADF antenna terminal A will be connected to the uhf receiver and terminal B will be terminated to ground through R1 and C1. During the next half cycle, with the polarities reversed, CR2 and CR4 will conduct while CR1 and CR3 are biased off. This causes the connections of the antenna terminals A and B to be reversed.

The functions of the other diode chopper components shown in Fig. 5 are the following: R1, together with the forward resistance of the diodes, terminates the antenna in its characteristic impedance of 51 ohms. C1, which approaches a short circuit for uhf frequencies, is used to isolate the 100-cps bias voltage from ground. If, however, the value of C1 were decreased, its reactance could be used to reduce the inductive reactance of the diode leads.

*Compared to a mechanical chopper which normally has a phase shift of approximately 10 degrees caused by contact travel time and mechanical inertia.

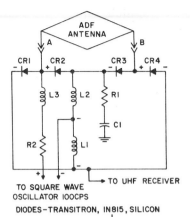

Fig. 5. Diode chopper schematic diagram.

TO SQUARE WAVE
OSCILLATOR 100CPS

DIODES–TRANSITRON, 1N815, SILICON
RI = RESISTOR-42 OHM, $\frac{1}{4}$ W, 1%
R2=RESISTOR-39 OHM, 2 W, 10%
C = CAPACITOR-15UUF, 2%, CERAMIC,
    TEMP COEFF –ZERO
L=CHOKE-RF, 2.7 UH, PHENOLIC CORE,
    500 MA DC

The three r-f chokes, L1, L2 and L3, isolate the r-f signal from the switching voltage source.

In the reverse biased condition the reverse voltage acts to decrease the diode shunt capacitance by increasing the junction barrier width. This, of course, is desirable since it results in an increase of reverse impedance. Conversely, this capacitance is increased when forward bias is applied to the diode. This also is a desirable feature. The bibliography can be consulted for further information on switching theory.

Diode Chopper Design and Construction

In the early phase of the search for a solid-state switch to be used in the ADF chopper, consideration was given to the use of saturable core windings as switching elements. Judging from the experiences of others at Collins Radio Company, however, it soon appeared unlikely that this type of a switch would satisfy ADF requirements beyond 100 megacycles, due to excessive shunt winding capacitance. Next, the use of a biased diode as a switching medium was investigated. High-frequency, small-area junction, high-conductance diodes appeared as the most likely to perform satisfactorily in this application. These proved to be suitable for use in the new switching device.

The first diodes tested were Hughes HD 2158 germanium and Transitron 1N815 silicon diodes. Tests of these diodes revealed that germanium diodes provide better switching action than silicon diodes. The reverse resistance was about the same, but germanium diodes exhibited a lower dynamic forward resistance than silicon diodes as shown in Table II, which represents average values.

Since germanium diodes cannot be used at temperatures exceeding 100 C, it was necessary to use silicon diodes. Contrary to expectations, the use of silicon diodes did not deteriorate the chopper operation, as was shown during later tests where it was compared

Table II. Forward Resistance Comparisons

Type	Average dynamic forward resistance
HD 2158 (germanium)	4.7 ohms at 48 ma
1N815 (silicon)	7.1 ohms at 48 ma

to a similar chopper using germanium diodes. Little difference was noted in overall system sensitivity. After both diode types were tested and proved to perform satisfactorily, no further attempt was made to evaluate other types. Undoubtedly, other types could perform as well or better in this application. From a survey of the literature it appears that P-i-N diodes would work well in this application. Unfortunately, P-i-N diodes do not appear to be available commercially.

After the selection of the diodes, the circuit shown in Fig. 5 was developed without much difficulty. Next came the packaging, where a great deal of experimenting was necessary to obtain the present case which exhibits good VSWR qualities. While attempting to obtain the best VSWR figure it was found that physical location of components inside the metal case is quite critical. The best arrangement was found to consist of mounting the diodes in a diamond-shaped combination as shown in Fig. 6 which shows the location of the parts before the chopper is filled with lockfoam. The lockfoam is used to reduce the possibility of wire or compo-

Fig. 6. Location of components inside the diode chopper.

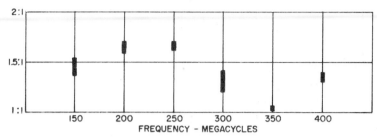

Fig. 7. VSWR measurements of six uhf ADF choppers using 1N815 diodes for switching.

nent breakage during shock and vibration. The foam increases the
chopper VSWR by a slight amount.

Diode Chopper Tests and Diode Data

During the design and later during the manufacture of the diode
chopper, extensive data was accumulated. It was thought that the
following topics could be of interest in future design.

VSWR

The greatest problem during the diode-chopper design was to
keep the attenuation of the received signal low. This meant keeping
the chopper insertion loss and the VSWR figure low throughout the
required frequency range of 225-400 megacycles. In regard to
VSWR, during the design a simplifying assumption was made that
the receiver has a resistive 51-ohm input impedance, and that the
antenna (without termination) has zero impedance in the 225 to 400-
megacycle frequency range. Both assumptions turned out to be
erroneous, but the impedances were such that they acted to reduce
the VSWR. Thus, during the chopper VSWR tests, it was noticed
that if a short wire was used to replace the ADF antenna, the
VSWR characteristics deteriorated. Also, during field tests, variation of the receiver input impedance with frequency appeared to be
the only way to explain the considerably higher sensitivity at some
frequencies. Figure 7 shows the VSWR variation versus frequency
of six diode choppers.

Diode Matching

After numerous experiments, it was found that the VSWR symmetry at uhf frequencies is improved by matching the dynamic forward resistances and the saturation voltages of the diodes. There
seemed to be little difference in diode chopper performance whether
matched diode quads or two matched diode pairs were used. Nev-
ertheless, it was decided to use matched diode quads, since these

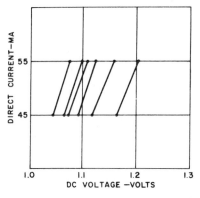

Fig. 8. Current-voltage characteristics of six 1N815 diodes.

present fewer possibilities for mistakes during assembly. Also, it
was found that compared to the amount of work it takes to obtain
matched diode pairs, only a little more work is required to obtain
matched diode quads.

The following procedure, proven in production, is used to match
diodes in quantities of less than 1000. The d-c voltage drop of each
diode for currents of 45 ma and 55 ma (supplied from a constant-
current generator) is measured and recorded. Then, according to
readings, the diodes are sorted into matched sets. Several readings
might look like those shown in the graph in Fig. 8. It is evident that
the diodes can be sorted according to saturation voltage and resistance slope with a reasonable proportion of importance given to
both. The matching is performed only at room temperature, as it
was determined that matched diodes stay reasonably well matched
throughout the required temperature range. Once the matching op-

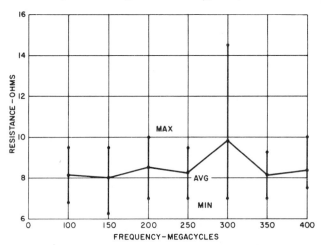

Fig. 9. Maximum and minimum resistance
of 1N815 diodes with 50-ma bias current vs.
frequency.

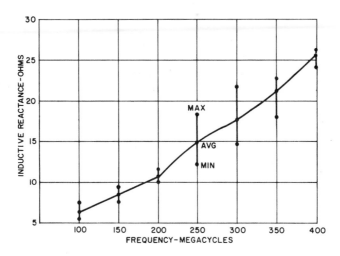

Fig. 10. Maximum, minimum, and average
reactance of 1N815 diodes with 50-ma d-c
bias current vs. frequency.

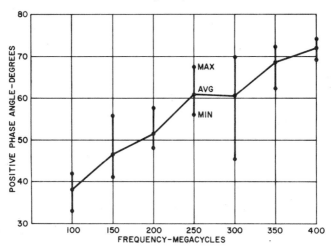

Fig. 11. Maximum, minimum, and average
phase angle of 1N815 diodes with 50-ma d-c
bias current vs. frequency.

eration is completed, a check is made by placing all four diodes of
a matched set into an r-f bridge circuit which indicates improper
matching by an excessive unbalance.

1N815 Data at 100-400 Megacycles

During efforts to reduce the diode chopper VSWR, it was thought
possible to measure the parameters of all chopper components

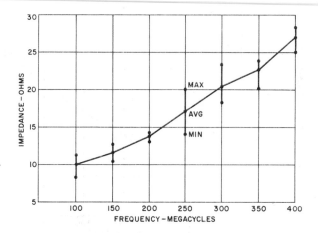

Fig. 12. Maximum, minimum, and average impedance of 1N815 diodes with 50-ma d-c bias current vs. frequency.

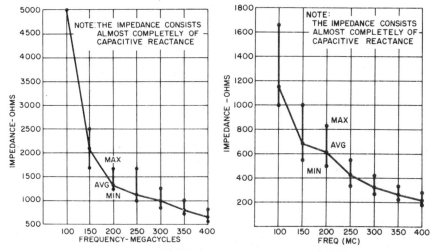

Fig. 13. Maximum, minimum, and average impedance of 1N815 diodes with -6 volts d-c reverse bias vs. frequency.

Fig. 14. Maximum, minimum and average impedance of 1N815 diodes with zero bias voltage vs. frequency.

separately and to use these values to calculate the theoretical values of VSWR and compare them with actual figures. In this way, the component values could be chosen to give minimum VSWR. Predictably, the theoretical and actual VSWR figures were not in sufficient agreement to be of practical design value. Among others, the reason for the difference undoubtedly was inaccuracy and variations of component impedance measurements. Although this experiment was not successful, it yielded some informative diode data. Thus, the data presented in Figs. 9 to 14 illustrate silicon diode impedance characteristics at various frequencies. This data was obtained from six diodes by using a General Radio 1607-A Transfer Function and Immittance Bridge. This bridge enables component impedance measurements independent of any stray capacitances to ground. Since the leads of the diodes tested were longer than those in the diode chopper circuit, there was an error in the diode impedance measurement due to excessive lead length. It was assumed that the excess lead inductance could be represented by an impedance in series with the diode impedance. Then this lead impedance was measured and subtracted from the diode impedance measurement. Thus, the data shown in Figs. 9 through 14 apply to diodes with 0.25 inch of lead length on both ends.

Conclusions

The preceding information demonstrates a practical application of a semiconductor switch as a uhf voltage chopper. The experience with the diode chopper thus far proved that in certain applications static switching devices can successfully compete with ordinary mechanical switches with regard to reliability, life, cost, size, weight, and electrical performance. Without doubt, there will be more frequent use of static switches in the near future as the knowledge in this field increases and becomes better known.

BIBLIOGRAPHY

1. Mattson, Roy H. and Samuel H. Leis, "Switching VHF Power Semiconductor Diodes," Proceedings of the National Electronics Conference, Volume 14, October 1958.
2. Uhlir, A., "The Potential of Semiconductor Diodes in High-Frequency Communications," Proceedings of the IRE, June 1958.
3. Armistead, M. A., E. G. Spencer and R. D. Hatcher, "Microwave Semiconductor Switch," Proceedings of the IRE, December 1956.
4. Millet, M. R., "Microwave Switching by Crystal Diodes," IRE Transactions on Microwave Theory and Techniques, July 1958.
5. Coale, F. S., "A Switch-Detector Circuit," IRE Transactions on Microwave Theory and Techniques, December 1955.
6. Knight, Geoffrey, Jr., editor. Semiconductor Electronics, Cambridge, Massachusetts.

11. Switching Characteristics of the Transwitch

ERIC JACKSON

Transitron Electronic Corporation
Wakefield, Massachusetts

Of the many types of four-layer PNPN devices available, the devices with gate switch-OFF characteristics most nearly approach the characteristics of the relay. This chapter describes the Transwitch, a PNPN switch, and gives some typical circuits.

Theory of Operation and Equivalent Circuit

The Transwitch, a three-terminal PNPN silicon device, is a bistable element that can be switched ON and OFF at the gate. To turn the Transwitch ON a positive pulse is applied to the gate and once the Transwitch has turned ON no more gate current need be supplied. A negative pulse at the gate switches the device OFF and the Transwitch stays OFF after the trigger pulse has been removed.

The operation of the Transwitch can be described by reference to the two-transistor equivalent circuit shown in Fig. 1. If the NPN transistor has current gain β_2 and the PNP transistor has current gain β_1 and the gate lead joint has current gain $\dfrac{\alpha_1 I_C + I_G}{\alpha_1 I_C}$ then the loop gain for the equivalent circuit can be written

$$\text{Loop Gain} = \left(\frac{\alpha_1 I_C + I_G}{\alpha_1 I_C}\right)\left(\frac{\alpha_1}{1 - \alpha_1}\right)\left(\frac{\alpha_2}{1 - \alpha_2}\right)$$

Since the current gain of a transistor is heavily dependent on the current flowing (being very small at low values of collector current and approaching a limiting value at higher currents), it fol-

126

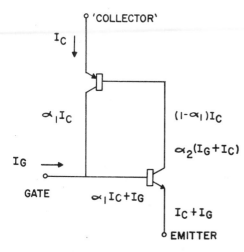

'COLLECTOR'

I_C

$\propto_1 I_C$

$(1-\propto_1)I_C$

$\propto_2(I_G+I_C)$

I_G

GATE

$\propto_1 I_C + I_G$

$I_C + I_G$

EMITTER

Fig. 1. Two-transistor equivalent circuit for describing operation of Transwitch.

lows that, depending on the value of gate current flowing, the loop gain can be less than, equal to, or greater than unity. If a current is injected into the gate sufficient to make the loop gain greater than unity, the two transistors will be driven into saturation and the switch will present a low impedance to the external circuit. The gate current may then be reduced to zero and the switch will stay in the ON state. Note that the current required to switch ON is dependent on the current gains of the two equivalent transistors and on the variation of current gain with gate current and is not dependent on the value of load current that finally flows.

To turn OFF the Transwitch a current must be withdrawn from the gate sufficient to make the loop gain of the two-transistor equivalent circuit fall below unity. If the beta of the top transistor is less than unity, then only a small fraction of the load current

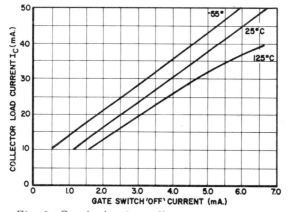

Fig. 2. Graph showing collector current vs. gate switch OFF current for the Transwitch at various temperatures.

flows in the collector of this transistor, and consequently a definite current gain exists between collector load current and gate switch OFF current. A graph of collector current vs. gate switch OFF current is shown in Fig. 2.

The Transwitch can also be turned ON and OFF at the collector. To switch the device ON, the collector voltage must be increased to the breakover voltage shown in the collector current-collector voltage characteristics of Fig. 3. At this point current multiplica-

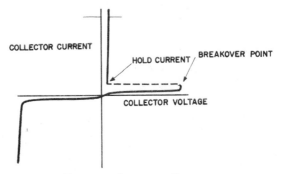

Fig. 3. Collector voltage—collector current characteristic of the Transwitch.

tion at the middle junction is sufficient to cause the current gain to increase and so make the loop gain greater than unity. Switch-OFF at the collector can be achieved by momentarily reducing the collector current to a value below the "hold" current. Switching at the collector involves the use of more power, but it may be convenient in certain applications.

The presently available Transwitches are intended for operation in the 5 to 50 mA range and up to 30 volts for the TSW-30 and 60 volts for the TSW-60. The gate current required to switch the device ON is below 1 mA and the gate current required to turn OFF 50 mA is 10 mA maximum. The forward current in the OFF condition and reverse current is typically less than 20 uA at 125 C.

Characteristics of Four-Layer Switches

Temperature Effects. At high ambient temperatures the increase in the leakage currents of the two equivalent transistors means that the current to be supplied from an external source to turn the Transwitch ON is reduced. This effect is enhanced by the increase in the betas of the two equivalent transistors with temperature increase. With the worst combination of parameters it is possible for the Transwitch to turn ON spontaneously when the gate is open circuited. For operation over a wide temperature range, current must be withdrawn from the gate sufficient to keep

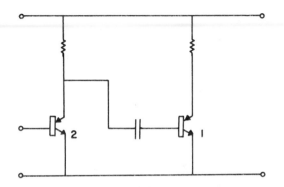

Fig. 4. Switching circuit.

the loop gain below unity. This bias current may be arranged by connecting a resistor from the gate to some negative voltage.

"Rate" Effect. The collector-to-emitter capacitance of a Transwitch if of the order of 5 pf at 10 volts. It is possible, using a fast transient of voltage at the collector, to cause sufficient current to flow via the capacitance to switch ON the device.

This effect should not be met with in the circuits and frequencies usual with presently available Transwitches. However, where Transwitches are in circuits involving mechanical contacts to apply collector voltages, care must be used to bias OFF the Transwitch sufficiently.

Capacitance Effect. If a capacitance is connected across a Transwitch and the saturation voltage is momentarily changed in some way (say by taking out of the gate a current just insufficient to switch the device OFF), then the charge taken by the capacitor may be sufficient to cause the current through the Transwitch to fall below the "hold" current, turning the Transwitch OFF. This effect may be used in some circuits to increase the apparent switch-OFF current gain.

Switching Speeds. To show the factors affecting switching speeds in a Transwitch circuit, the circuit of Fig. 4 is considered. Assume that the frequency of operation is such that the circuit time constants are small compared with the period of switching.

If Transwitch No. 2 is switched OFF then the gate current waveform at Transwitch No. 1 will have a peak value of $\Delta V/R_g$ where ΔV is the collector voltage swing of the previous stage and R_g the gate resistance of Transwitch No. 1, and will decay with a time constant CR_g. For the switch OFF process to be successful, the gate switch OFF current pulse has to be longer than the collector storage and transient time. Let the value of C that makes this so be C_g, so that the time constant is $C_g R_g$. If the switch-OFF current gain were now increased by a factor n, then the maximum current excursion at the gate could be reduced to 1/nth, say by increasing R_g. The time constant may now be reduced to its original value by making C_g go to C_g/n. This means that the capacitance

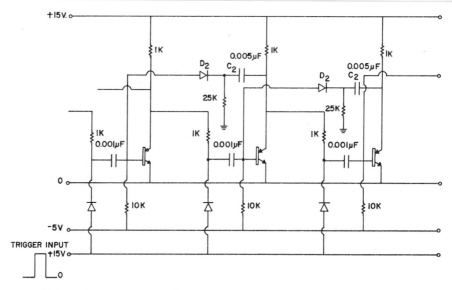

Fig. 5. Ring counter, a basic circuit in computer-type equipment.

loading at the previous stage has been reduced to 1/nth of its previous value. Therefore, other things being equal, a device with a higher switch-OFF beta can be used at a higher frequency in circuits.

Typical Circuits

The following circuits are given as an indication of the types of circuit function the Transwitch will perform.

Ring Counters. The ring counter is a basic circuit in any computer-type equipment. It performs the functions of a timing waveform generator usually driven directly from the clock generator. Figure 5 shows such a ring counter. It is assumed that prior to the triggering pulse being applied one Transwitch is put into the ON state and all other Transwitches are OFF. All diodes except the one connected to the ON stage are reverse biased. This forward biased diode allows the triggering pulse to be applied to the gate of the subsequent stage turning the Transwitch ON. The negative-going transient occurring at the collector of this Transwitch is passed via capacitor C_2 and Diode D_2 to the gate of the preceding stage and turns this Transwitch OFF. The ON state has been passed from one stage to the next at a frequency determined by the triggering pulse. The output pulse goes from +15 volts to +1 volt. A circuit giving a pulse going from +1 volt to +15 volts can be provided by reversing the direction of the diodes and by making $C_1 = 0.001$ uf and $C_2 = 0.005$ uf.

If circuit simplicity is extremely important then the ring counter

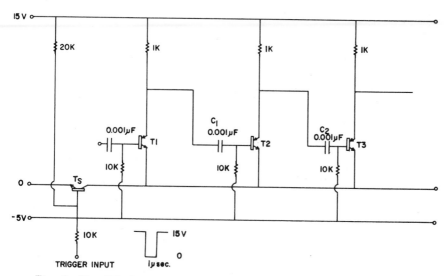

Fig. 6. Simplified ring counter whose speed of operation is less than that of the circuit of Fig. 5.

of Fig. 6 can be used with some loss in speed. Again it is assumed that prior to the triggering pulse being applied, one Transwitch is put into the ON state and all other Transwitches are OFF. If now the series Transistor T_S is momentarily switched OFF, the current through the ON Transwitch will be discontinued and the collector voltage will rise from $+1$ volt to $+15$ volts. This positive going transient is passed via capacitor C_1 to the gate of the subsequent Transwitch. If now the series transistor T_S is momentarily switched OFF, the current through the ON Transwitch will be discontinued and the collector voltage will rise from $+1$ volt to $+15$

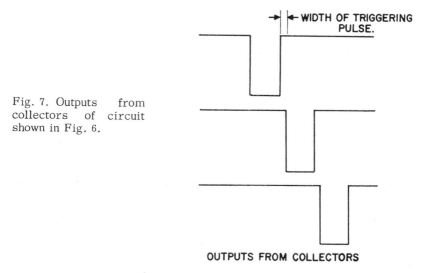

Fig. 7. Outputs from collectors of circuit shown in Fig. 6.

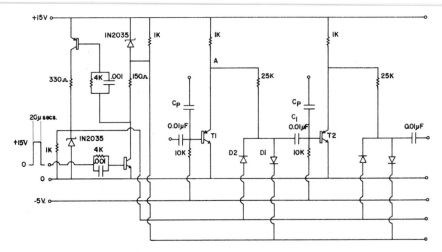

Fig. 8. Shift register circuit.

volts. This positive-going transient is passed via capacitor C_1 to the gate of the subsequent Transwitch. If now the series transistor is switched ON again before the positive voltage at the gate of T_2 has decayed below the switch-ON voltage, then this Transwitch will turn ON, the preceding one remaining OFF. The output waveform from this circuit is shown in Fig. 7, the gap between the pulses being the width of the triggering pulse.

Shift Register. The shift register circuit in a computer accepts information in the form of pulses in parallel and transmits the in-

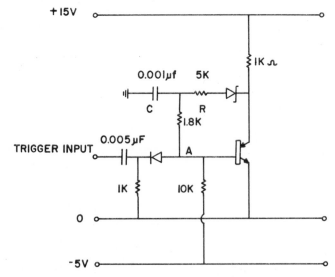

Fig. 9. Monostable circuit used for fixed delay between input and output.

formation in a serial form. A circuit to perform this function is shown in Fig. 8.

The triggering pulses are provided by the transistor circuit shown. The Zener diodes ensure a fixed pulse height. The triggering circuit chosen will depend on the number of stages driven, the circuit shown being used to drive four stages. The purpose of the triggering circuit is to switch a stage into the state of the previous one.

Assuming that T_1 is OFF, then Point A is at $+15$ volts and D_1 is forward biased. The negative-going pulse from the trigger source is passed via diode D_1 and C_1 to the gate of the next stage to turn the Transwitch OFF. If T_1 is ON, then D_2 is forward biased and the positive going pulse from the trigger source is passed via D_2 and C_1 to the gate of T_2 to switch it ON. Information into the shift register is inserted in parallel via capacitors C_p.

Monostable Circuit. The monostable circuit is used where a

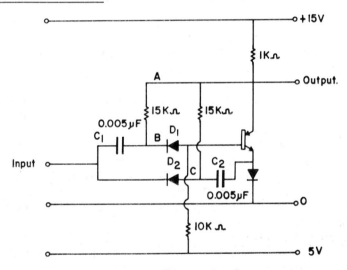

Fig. 10. Binary circuit.

fixed delay is required between input and output. The Transwitch shown in Fig. 9 has a preferred ON state. If a negative pulse is applied to the input the Transwitch turns OFF and the collector voltage begins to rise to the supply voltage. When the collector voltage reaches the Zener diode voltage, the Zener diode allows a charging current to pass to the capacitor. When the voltage at Point A has risen to the gate switch-ON voltage, the Transwitch again turns ON and remains ON until the next trigger pulse is applied. The time between switch-OFF and switch-ON is dependent on the time constant CR. In the circuit shown the output pulse width is approximately 15 microseconds when triggered at frequencies up to 20 kc.

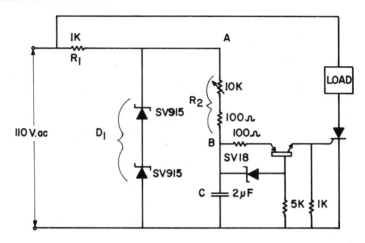

Fig. 11. Controlled rectifier trigger circuit.

Binary Circuit. The binary circuit of Fig. 10 performs the counting function required in many computer-type circuits. It provides an output which is at half the frequency of the input.

Assume that the Transwitch is initially OFF. Points A, B, and C are all at + 15 volts. When the input is applied, diode D_2 is forward biased and the voltage at Point C follows the input voltage. This causes the gate emitter diode to become forward biased and turns the Transwitch ON. The collector voltage drops to + 1 volt. Points A, B, and C are now at 1 volt. The next trigger pulse that is applied is passed via capacitor C_1 and is superimposed on the 1 volt at Point B. The diode D_1 becomes forward biased and the negative pulse is passed to the gate to switch the Transwitch OFF. The frequency of the output waveform is therefore one-half of the frequency of the input waveform.

Controlled Rectifier Trigger Circuit. The trigger circuit shown in Fig. 11 can be used where it is required to turn ON the controlled rectifier at a certain point in the voltage cycle. The resistance R_1 and Zener diode D_1 ensure that the voltage at Point B does not exceed 30 volts. When the voltage at this point passes through zero, the capacitor C charges via R_1. When the voltage at Point B reaches the Zener diode voltage, current passes to the gate of the Transwitch to turn it ON. The capacitor then discharges through the Transwitch into the gate of the controlled rectifier to switch it ON. The conduction angle of the controlled rectifier can be varied by varying the charging time of the capacitor, i.e. by varying R_1.

12. Control Circuit Applications of the Silicon Controlled Switch

LLOYD H. DIXON, Jr.

Solid State Products, Inc.
Salem, Massachusetts

The Silicon PNPN Controlled Switch is a relatively new solid state switching device that is finding wide usage as a control circuit element. Unique characteristics of the controlled switch have opened many new design approaches resulting in major circuit simplification, size and weight reduction, and increased reliability. These properties include: high sensitivity or gain, high voltage and current handling capability, and higher efficiency than silicon transistors of comparable size. The controlled switch is a pulse operated device, and its inherent memory is a useful tool in control circuit logic.

Characteristics

Output characteristics of the controlled switch (Fig. 1) are basically the same as the silicon controlled rectifier. In a miniature JEDEC TO-9 package, the controlled switch is rated at 1.25 amp DC at 100 C case temperature, with peak pulse and surge ratings up to 30 amp.

The controlled switch differs from the silicon controlled rectifier in one important aspect: much higher sensitivity and closer control of gate firing characteristics. Figure 2 shows gate firing current of a high sensitivity controlled switch type as a function of temperature (98 percent distribution limits). The specification guarantees a maximum limit of 20 μA at 25 C. Current gain of 50,000 and power gain of 1,000,000 is easily achieved with this device.

The lower limit of the distribution in Fig. 2 indicates that some

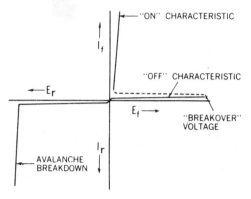

Fig. 1. Output characteristic.

units may fire, at a negative value of gate current. Because of the high sensitivity of these devices, some units may fire due to their own internal leakage current. This effect, similar to βI_{CBO} in a transistor, is easily overcome by supplying a negative bias current to the gate.

Figure 3 shows the gate firing voltage characteristic of the same controlled switch type. Gate firing voltage declines as temperature increases because of the negative temperature coefficient of the gate-cathode junction. Since the gate must reach a definite positive potential before firing occurs, a resistor connected between gate and cathode provides adequate bias stabilization up to 125 C.

Threshold Detectors

As shown in Fig. 2, the total variation of gate firing current for all units ranges from + 50 µA at − 55 C to − 20 µA at + 125 C. Al-

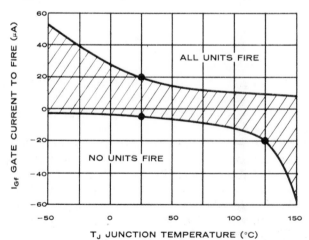

Fig. 2. Gate firing current.

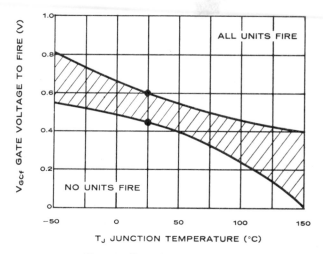

Fig. 3. Gate firing voltage.

though the range of gate firing current is large in a relative sense, the magnitude is extremely small in relation to the current handling ability of the device. A negative gate bias source of 20 μA would be required for bias stabilization at 125 C. If, however, a negative gate bias of 1 mA is applied, the total input current required to fire the controlled switch will range from 1.05 mA at −55 C to 0.98 mA at +125 C. Thus, by "swamping out" the gate firing current of the controlled switch with a relatively large amount of negative bias, a firing current threshold is established with an accuracy of a few percent. With greater negative bias, accuracy is proportionately improved at the expense of overall sensitivity.

The current threshold detector can be converted into a voltage threshold detector by adding an appropriate resistor in series with the input (Fig. 4). Another technique for establishing a voltage threshold is the series Zener diode (Fig. 5). In this case, negative bias can be reduced to the level required for stabilization, thereby improving the current sensitivity of the circuit. The positive temperature coefficient of a 7-volt Zener will compensate for the negative temperature coefficient of the gate firing voltage of the controlled switch.

Controlled switch current and voltage threshold detectors are the basis for many different circuit applications. Current threshold accuracy simplifies complex AND and OR control logic circuits. Voltage threshold detectors can sense power supply overvoltage and the controlled switch with its high output current capability will operate in a fraction of a microsecond to protect sensitive load elements.

The voltage threshold detector combined with an RC timing network forms the simple time delay static switching circuit shown in

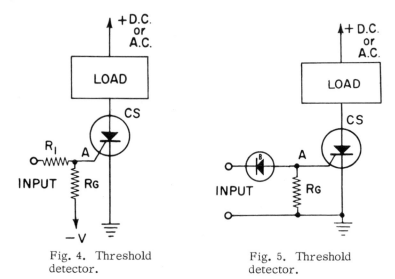

Fig. 4. Threshold detector.

Fig. 5. Threshold detector.

Fig. 6. Because of the high sensitivity of the controlled switch, time delays of 0.1 sec/ufd are achieved. For long time delays, accuracy depends on the stability and leakage of the capacitor.

An illustration of circuit simplification using the controlled switch is in firing squibs for explosive bolts and rocket engine ignition. A time delay is generally necessary. Three to five transistors would be required, including a power transistor capable of supplying several amperes for a few milliseconds. A single miniature controlled switch will do the same job.

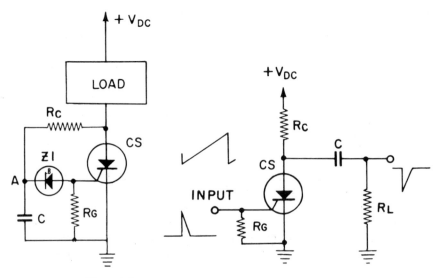

Fig. 6. Time delay static switch.

Fig. 7. RC pulse generator.

Pulse Generators

PNPN devices are excellent switching elements for high level pulse generating circuits because of their high efficiency and current handling ability. Also, once the controlled switch is fired, it will carry as much current as the load dictates, minimizing drive requirements. Most controlled switch pulse generating circuits operate by discharging an energy storage element into the load. In this manner, the pulse current is not drawn directly from the power supply, and means are easily provided to turn off the controlled switch once the pulse energy has been delivered.

Figure 7 shows a simple RC pulse generator that can deliver pulses of several amperes with input drive of only a fraction of a milliampere. If the charging resistor R_c is made large enough so that the available charging current is less than the "dropout" current of the controlled switch, it will automatically turn off allowing the capacitor to recharge. Variations of this circuit can be made free running with electronically variable repetition rate. They are easily synchronized for pulse frequency divider applications. A compact and reliable phase variable pulse generator circuit employing the miniature controlled switch can directly drive the highest power silicon controlled rectifiers in proportional power control applications.

By substituting a two-terminal pulse forming network for the capacitor in Fig. 7, a rectangular pulse will be delivered to the load. This circuit is the same in principle as the hydrogen thyratron pulse modulators used in radar systems. If the load resistance is slightly smaller than the characteristic impedance of the pulse forming network, anode voltage across the controlled switch will reverse after the end of the pulse, automatically turning it off. Charging chokes can be employed for resonant recharge of the pulse forming network.

The controlled switch is now being used in several different radar beacon modulator applications, delivering pulses of 0.5 to 2.0 microseconds width and 2 to 20 amp in amplitude. Rise time capabilities are 0.1 us to 1 amp and 0.2 us to 20 amp.

Referring again to the circuit of Fig. 7, an inductance can be inserted in series with the capacitor and load resistor. Now, when the controlled switch fires, the capacitor must discharge through the inductor and the load. If the load resistance is small compared to the reactances of the inductor and capacitor at resonance, a damped train of oscillations would commence. However, only the first half cycle of oscillation can occur, since the controlled switch will block the negative half. The anode is then left at a negative voltage which automatically turns off the controlled switch. A full sinusoid output can be obtained by connecting a diode in inverse parallel across the controlled switch. This type of LC pulse generator has been used to drive magnetic cores, where the inductance of the core string forms part of the total inductance of the circuit.

AC-DC Output Techniques

The controlled switch, with its thyratron-like properties, can be turned on easily, but turning it off is frequently a serious problem. In low speed circuits, where "memory" is not desired, an a-c anode power supply should be used, since it provides for automatic turnoff of the controlled switch with each negative half cycle of the

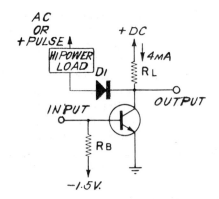

Fig. 8. Combined logic and power control.

supply voltage. As long as a control signal is present on the gate of the controlled switch, it will apply rectified direct current to the load. Where memory is desired, a d-c supply is generally used, with turn off accomplished by any one of several brute force techniques which involve either driving the anode temporarily negative, shunting the load current away from the controlled switch, or opening the anode circuit.

The Trigistor is a new PNPN device similar to the controlled switch which can be turned off as well as on at the control input terminal. When the Trigistor is turned on, it can switch up to 1 ampere of load current. However, at the present time, turn-off control at the base input terminal is possible only if the load current is less than 100 mA. The Trigistor is primarily used as a bistable logic element in simplified binary counter, ring counter, shift register, and Schmitt trigger circuits.

As the turn-off capability of the Trigistor is pushed to higher current levels, more simplification of static switching circuits will be possible. Even with the present limitations on turn off control at the base, the Trigistor is an extremely versatile static switching element. For example, in the circuit of Fig. 8, the Trigistor serves double duty as a low level logic element and a high level static switch. This is based on the fact that once the Trigistor has been turned on, it will carry whatever current the load dictates, regardless of any other consideration. In this case, the Trigistor has two separate loads. Assume, for the moment, that diode D_1 and the high power load are disconnected. The balance of the circuit could represent a portion of a logic circuit, such as a shift register or binary counter stage. When the Trigistor is on, it carries a collector current of 4 mA through R_L. At this level, it can easily be turned off by means of a negative pulse applied to the base terminal. When the Trigistor is off, its collector voltage is equal to the collector d-c supply voltage. Now, with the diode and high power load back in the circuit as shown, if the high power load is connected to an a-c supply bus, D_1 will block whenever the a-c voltage is negative. Trigistor collector current cannot exceed 4 mA, and the Trigistor can be turned on and off in accomplishing its function as a logic circuit element. When the a-c voltage commences to go positive, if the Trigistor is off, its collector is at the positive d-c supply voltage, and D_1 will continue to block provided the d-c supply voltage is greater than the peak positive a-c voltage. However, if the Trigistor happens to be on as a result of logic operations, it and D_1 will conduct current to the high power load. During this period of high current flow, the Trigistor cannot be turned off, so that logic functions and high level output functions must be accomplished on a time sharing basis. During each negative half cycle, one or hundreds of logic operations can be performed.

Pulse power can be used instead of ac to operate the high power loads. At the conclusion of a sequence of logic operations, readout is obtained by applying a positive voltage pulse to the bus connected to the high power loads. Loads such as print hammers, solenoids, magnetic clutches and brakes, relays, etc. are within the current handling ability of the Trigistor.

13. Silicon Semiconductor Switches for Static Relay Applications

W. F. MUNZER and E. W. TOROK

Semiconductor Department
Westinghouse Electric Corp.
Youngwood, Pennsylvania

The Trinistor controlled rectifier is a three-terminal NPNP silicon device which exhibits bistable characteristics similar to those of thyratrons, magnetic amplifiers, switching transistors, and electromechanical relays. The three terminals comprise two emitters and a gate or control terminal. Figure 1 is a block diagram showing the basic structure of the NPNP silicon switch. The proposed AIEE symbol, for all devices of this type, is included here to show corresponding terminal designations and applied voltage polarities. Current flow is from anode to cathode. The gate is

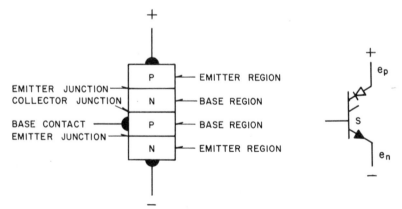

Fig. 1. Basic structure (left) and symbol of Trinistor NPNP silicon switch.

142

bias-positive with respect to the cathode for forward current conduction.

The non-linear control characteristic of the Trinistor controlled rectifier is well suited to applications requiring the control of large quantities of power with minimum power input. For comparison purposes a 50-amp transistor, having a current gain of 10, requires a continuous 5 amp to drive it to full output. The 50-amp Trinistor requires only 50 ma maximum gate current to switch the device.

The device characteristics discussed here are typical for a 100-amp Trinistor. With the exception of current rating, devices of 1 to 100 amp have similar characteristics. Topics discussed here are device fabrication, basic electrical characteristics, device current capacity, advantages as a static relay, and Trinistor applications.

Fabrication

Referring to Fig. 2, the Trinistor is a solid-state switch which utilizes a basic NPNP structure. The starting material used to fabricate this switch is an N-type silicon single crystal slice. Two

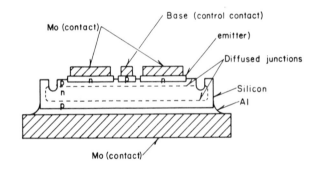

Fig. 2. Schematic cross-section of Trinistor.

P-type regions are made by diffusing aluminum, boron, or gallium one to two mils into the starting material. The resultant structure of the original N-type material becomes PNP after diffusion with no dimensional change. One of the P-regions and adjacent N-region become base layers. The other P-region becomes the positive emitter or collector. A fourth region, N-type is made by alloying an N-type alloy with the diffused P-type base, converting a thin region to N-type. This thin N-type region becomes the negative emitter. During the same fusion operation, two contacts are made, one to the P-type base where the control electrode is attached and the second to the positive emitter or collector. After this fusion operation the diffused PNP structure becomes the basic

NPNP device with only a slight increase in overall thickness (~0.003 mils).

The remaining fabrication operations consist of lead attachment to the positive and negative emitters, base, and the encapsulation of the unit. Molybdenum sections are hard soldered to basic units in various critical areas of the unit to protect it from thermal stresses and fatigue during actual operation. The unit is hard soldered to a copper base and painted with varnish to protect the surfaces of the unit from any contamination. A ceramic seal is then welded to the copper base. A vacuum is pulled within the double-ended case and back filled with an inert gas. Finally, external leads are attached to the unit, and the Trinistor is complete for application.

Electrical Characteristics

The basic electrical characteristics together with symbols and nomenclature are illustrated in Fig. 3. The Trinistor has two states in the forward direction, an OFF state and an ON state, which permits its use as a switch or relay. In the forward direc-

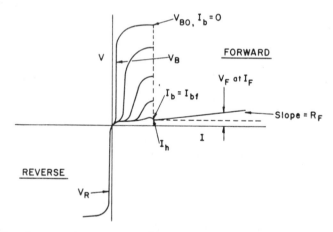

V_{BO}	Breakover voltage at zero base current at room temperature
V_R	Rated reverse voltage at specified leakage current
V_B	Rated forward blocking voltage at specified leakage current
V_F	Forward voltage drop at specified current and junction temperature
R_F	Differential resistance of device in the ON state
I_{bf}	Base firing current
V_{bf}	Emitter-base voltage necessary to drive I_{bf}
I_h	Minimum current through device to hold in ON state
T_{ON}	Switch-on time to specified load current from initiation of turn-on pulse to 10 percent of initial blocking voltage
T_{OFF}	Switch-off time from specified load current (including storage time) to 90 percent of final blocking voltage

Fig. 3. Basic voltage-current characteristics.

tion the collector junction, shown in Fig. 1, will block until a critical voltage V_{BO} and current I_{BO} are reached. The device will then go into a hyperconductive state permitting high forward current I_F to flow. Conduction will continue until the forward current is reduced below the holding current I_h. The device will then switch to a high impedance state blocking in the forward direction. The breakover voltage at which conduction occurs may be reduced to a few volts by a relatively small gate current I_{bf} at a small gate voltage V_{bf}.

In the reverse direction the blocking action is similar to a reverse-bias silicon power rectifier. The rated reverse voltage V_R can have the same value as the forward blocking voltage. However, it must not be the final criterion in determining its applicability in a particular circuit. Certain circuits do not require a device which has a high blocking reverse voltage. In fact, paralleling diodes are often used to eliminate this characteristic for a return current path.

In Fig. 3 breakover voltage V_{BO} is a function of gate current I_{bf}. The current required to fire the 100-ampere Trinistor at room temperature can be as great as 100 ma for gate voltages of 1 to 3 volts. The gate current I_{bf} is lower at elevated junction temperatures. The maximum allowable current which the gate circuit may conduct is limited by the size of gate lead. Little advantage is gained by driving the device with excessive gate current except in circuits requiring extremely fast turn-on times.

Typical switching times, depending on the circuits used, for the 100-amp device are as follows:

Turn-on time (τ_{on})
    Delay time   1.0 - 10 us
    Rise time   0.2 - 0.9 us
Turn-off time (τ_{off})
    Storage time   6 - 21 us
    Recovery time   35 - 45 us

Current Carrying Capacity

The current carrying capability of Trinistors is limited by loss of control function attributed to increased leakage currents at high operating junction temperature. The junction temperature depends upon the total power which must be dissipated at the junction and total thermal resistance. The losses occurring during the OFF condition in the larger silicon power devices are negligible. But the ON losses can be quite large, especially for extremely high power devices. This loss is the product of the forward voltage drop and operating current. Figure 4 shows the instantaneous forward voltage drop at various instantaneous currents.

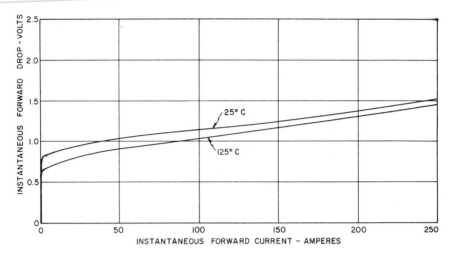

Fig. 4. Typical forward drop as a function
of load current.

The total thermal resistance consists of junction-to-case and case-to-heat sink resistances. In most power device applications operating in convection or forced liquid or air cooling, the latter resistance predominates. The thermal resistance from junction to case is a subject for device design consideration. The thermal resistance for the 100-amp Trinistor has values varying from 0.2 to

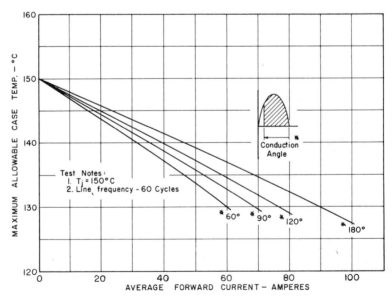

Fig. 5. Maximum allowable case temperature as a function of conduction angle and forward current.

Comparison of Trinistor With Electromagnetic Relay and Magnetic Amplifier

Property	Trinistor	Electromagnetic relay	Magnetic amplifier
Switching time Turn-on Turn-off	10.9 us max 66 us	250 us and greater	Terms of fractional portions of power line frequency
Switching power requirements	100 mA at 3 V max	Dependent upon size —mA to A	—
OFF-state resistance	40K ohms and higher	Very high	High with low leakage diodes
ON-state resistance	0.1 ohm or less	1 ohm or less	Resistance of inductor windings
Size	Small—8 oz for 100-A size	Dependent upon application—oz to lb	Large compared to other devices of equivalent power and current rating
Contact bounce	None	Measurable	None
Shock and vibration	No difficulty	Effects minimized by suitable design	Good
Life	Measured in terms of thousands of hours of operation	Measured in terms of operations—10K operations and greater	Measured in terms of thousands of hours of operation

0.4 C/watt. The maximum current rating shown by Fig. 5 was determined by power testing the device at a junction temperature of 150 C. The rated breakover voltage was maintained during these tests. Ratings can be extended by water cooling. Load tests were conducted for currents exceeding 200 amp average half-wave current at case temperatures approaching 100 C.

Advantages of Trinistors

Comparisons are shown between the Trinistor and conventional electromagnetic switching devices in the accompanying table. The comparisons show that a Trinistor switch is equal to or better than other types of control devices and possesses relatively few of their disadvantages.

Applications

The newest semiconductor switch is a natural for static a-c switch circuitry. The Trinistor can be used in applications requiring control of either large or small load currents with relatively small gate currents. Direct current may also be switched by properly designed circuits. Static control of electric motors is obtainable. This includes both starting and speed control equipment. Immediate applications for power conversions are apparent. Westinghouse has demonstrated the use of high power Trinistor controlled rectifiers in static inverters designed for military and commercial end use.

Trinistor-produced d-c to d-c power conversion, for mobile and fixed station communication equipment, has features attractive for the military. In comparison to vibrator and dynamotor power supplies, static supplies offer noiseless operation. Mechanical and electrical design difficulties associated with movable contacts, commutation and brush problems, bearings, and sparking at high altitude operation are eliminated. What does elimination of these problems mean to the military services? Equipment reliability.

Current Ratings

A series of silicon semiconductor switches are required to cover the broad power ranges found in instrumentation and control. Trinistor for current ratings of 1, 10, 50, and 100 amp average forward current have been fabricated. Operation of the 100-amp switch at 200 amp by water cooling shows feasibility for still larger devices.

14. Design of Static Power Relays, Contactors, and Circuit Breakers

EDWARD DEMERS

Walter Kidde & Company, Inc.
Belleville, New Jersey

The rapid evolution of solid state components and the associated advances in circuit design have resulted in important advances in control and switching elements. The static relay and static contactor are probably among the most important of these new devices. Static relays and static contactors are now available having contact power ratings ranging from milliwatts to kilowatts. They have the advantages over more conventional devices of very fast response, long life, and high reliability under adverse environmental conditions. They avoid many of the problems of mechanical relays such as contact contamination, contact bounce, and malfunction under shock and vibration. They are differentiated from static switching, gating, and amplifying circuits by: (a) Snap action on and off, (b) electrical isolation between actuating and load circuits, and (c) no interaction between actuating and load signals.

Walter Kidde & Company has been active in this field and has developed a variety of static relays and static contactors. Some of these are shown in Fig. 1. An 18-amp a-c static contactor is shown in Fig. 2 and a 10-amp d-c motor starting relay is shown in Fig. 3. A static light flasher, shown in Fig. 4, is used to turn on and off the exterior lights of an aircraft and is subject to the heavy inrush currents of the incandescent lamps at the start of each cycle. The static flasher is mechanically and electrically interchangeable with the existing light flasher, sells for approximately the same price, and extends the maintenance-free operating life

149

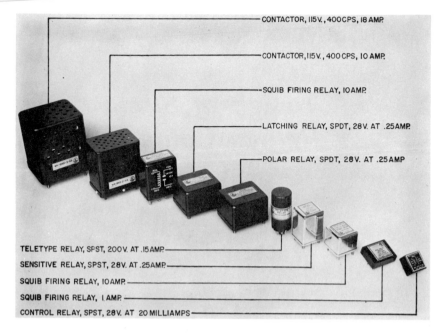

Fig. 1. Typical static relays.

from a few hundred hours for the mechanical unit to 10,000 hours and more for the static device.

Static relays, circuit breakers, and similar solid-state devices are effective supplements to the mechanical units, but are not a panacea. They are not intended to replace all electromechanical relays and circuit breakers. When properly applied, however, they represent a new level of performance capability and reliability. Because of this, static relays will find application where reliability and performance are both of great importance.

Silicon Controlled Rectifier

The power relay, contactor, and circuit breaker must be used with the new silicon controlled rectifiers which have the inherent properties of:

1. High voltage and current ratings—up to 400 volts with inrush currents up to 500 amp.

2. High junction temperature ratings—up to 150 C.

3. High surge current rating—over ten times the average current rating.

4. Low forward voltage drop when conducting—typically 1 volt.

5. Fast turn-on and turn-off times—typically 1 to 20 microseconds

6. Low power actuation requirements—typically 100 milliwatts.

Fig. 2. A typical 18-amp a-c static contactor.

Fig. 3. A 10-amp d-c motor starting relay.

Fig. 4. Static light flasher for exterior lights of an aircraft.

The AC Contact

An a-c contact may be made, as shown in Fig. 5, by using two controlled rectifiers in a back-to-back configuration, and this contact will conduct in both directions when both gates are properly actuated. The primary design problem is to actuate the gates from a control signal which is electrically isolated, and to maintain the following design parameters:

1. The gate must be fully actuated for at least 60 degrees before and after the line voltage passes through zero so that the appropriate controlled rectifier will be ready for conduction at the time of zero current crossover even for small load power factors.

2. When the control signal is removed, the gate excitation must return to zero almost instantaneously so that the contact will turn off the next time the load current passes through zero crossover.

3. The gates of the controlled rectifier are the most delicate part of the unit, and it is of primary importance to achieve full excitation without exceeding their power dissipation ratings and

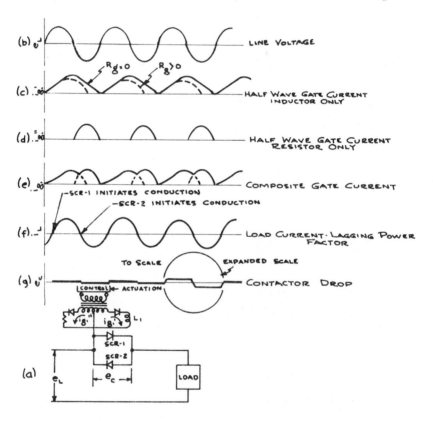

Fig. 5. Circuit of typical a-c static relay (a) and its operating waveforms.

without reversing the gate voltage beyond the values specified. Using the type C35 silicon controlled rectifier as a design example, the gate actuation requirements are achieved for all conditions of operation by applying approximately 6 volts to the gate through a 300-ohm series resistor. If this load line is superimposed upon the gate actuation requirements, the gate power dissipation is at all times within the allowable ratings and that regardless of changes in the gate characteristics from unit to unit and with temperature, the gate is fully excited.

The gate power may be derived from the power supply by means of a small transformer rectifier. However, this circuit is inadequate in that the gate voltage goes to zero at the time that the line voltage passes through zero which is, of course, the worst possible instant. This objection may be overcome by a capacitor storage circuit, but this type of circuit has the disadvantage of slowly decaying after the control signal is removed, with a correspondingly slow turnoff time.

The operation of this circuit is shown in Figs. 5b through 5g. The line supply voltage is plotted in Fig. 5b. The gate current with a half-wave rectifier and the inductor L1 only is shown in Fig. 5c, and the maximum gate current occurs when the line voltage passes through zero, and this gate current is maintained for a considerable conduction angle. However, the curve ($R_g = 0$) is idealistic and the actual gate current ($R_g > 0$) is illustrated in the dashed line. A detailed analysis shows that the current is not generally sustained for a great enough angle to give reliable operation of the contact for all conditions of power factor, and it is desirable to supplement this gate current as shown in Fig. 5d. This is derived with a simple half-wave rectifier operating on the alternate half cycles of supply, and the composite gate current is shown in Fig. 5e. Relatively large gate currents are supplied for power factor variations from 0 lagging to 0 leading, and the second important criteria of the gate current returning to zero within the cycle of line frequency is also achieved. The need for gate excitation over a considerable angular range is illustrated by the line current shown in Fig. 5f, and the typical drop across the static contact e_c is shown in Fig. 5g. This is typically 1 volt and results in only minor waveform distortions and minor voltage regulation characteristics. The typical operation of the contact is shown in Fig. 6 illustrating the time delay in closing, the transient current in the initial cycles, and the time delay in opening with a controlled rectifier.

The first cycle of load current can look highly inductive and can lag by more than 90 degrees in its point of zero crossover under certain conditions. It is especially important to be aware of this starting transient to avoid malfunction under certain load condi-

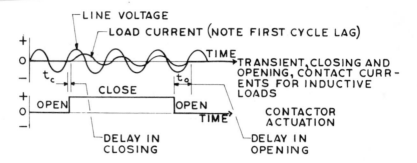

Fig. 6. Curves for transient operation of static contact with inductive load.

tions, and this is taken care of by the gate excitation circuit shown in Fig. 5. The time delay in opening is determined by the time for the gate excitation to reduce to zero (which is very rapid in this case) and by the additional time for the line current to pass through zero which will permit the controlled rectifier to extinguish.

The full schematic diagram of a typical a-c power relay is shown in Fig. 7 where a transistor switching circuit is inserted in a full-wave diode bridge. The transistor is used to program the a-c power from the supply to the gate circuits. The control circuit is completely isolated electrically from the load circuit and no power is drawn from the line except when the unit is actuated. This simple circuit requires a step input which may be de-

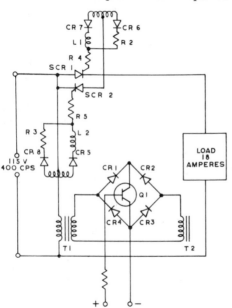

Fig. 7. Circuit diagram of a-c static contactor.

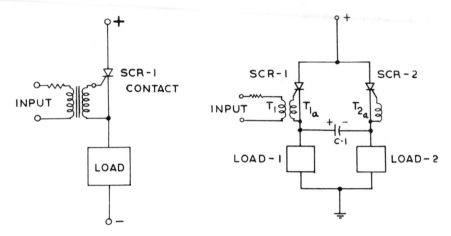

Fig. 8. Circuit of simple latch-   Fig. 9. Circuit of simple SPDT
ing contactor.   d-c static relay.

rived from a large number of bistable circuit elements or by a
static relay.

Design of DC Contacts

The design of a static latching d-c contact is very simple (Fig.
8) in that it utilizes a single controlled rectifier with a transformer coupled to the actuating source. A pulse input turns the
contact on and it remains on until the supply power is removed.
There are many applications for this simple type of d-c contact
for squib firing, arming, programming, and similar circuits, but
for the general application it is necessary to develop d-c contacts
capable of turnoff as well as turnon.

Turnoff may be achieved as shown in Fig. 9. If SPST operation
is desired, it is a simple matter to substitute a lower power
dummy load in place of load No. 2. Operation is the same as before in that when a positive pulse is applied to the input terminals,
SCR-1 will be turned on. The commutating capacitor C1 will be
charged as shown, and the relay is now ready for operation. When
a negative pulse is applied to the input, SCR-2 is turned on, applying power to load No. 2, and the potential at the anode of SCR-2
rises by an amount equal to the supply voltage. Since the capacitor
cannot instantaneously discharge, the cathode of SCR-1 instantaneously rises well above the supply voltage, causing SCR-1 to turn
off. The capacitor C1 then rapidly discharges through load No. 1,
and load No. 1 is now open circuited. There is a short make-be-
fore-break operation in the neighborhood of 50 to 100 microseconds. The circuit shown can be cycled at rates up to 500 cps and is
quite satisfactory where the loads are fixed and the transient spike
on the load just prior to turnoff is not objectionable. However, for

many applications, a more sophisticated turnoff circuit is desirable, as shown in Fig. 10. In this design, the voltage rise above the supply voltage is limited by diodes CR-1 and CR-2, and they provide a path for the circulating current during the turnoff interval. The time duration is determined primarily by the LC time constant, and the capacitor charge is reversed and stored during the turnoff interval and is not dissipated in the load. The net result is that the load voltage does not rise above the supply voltage during turnoff and the turnoff time is controlled by a tuned circuit and is relatively independent of the load impedance.

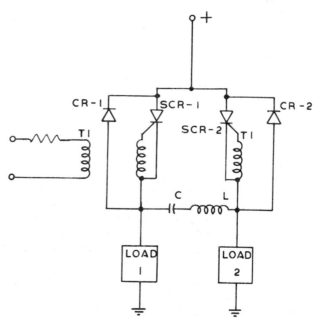

Fig. 10. Circuit of a SPDT d-c static relay.

This type of relay can be designed for d-c supply voltages from 28 to 400 volts and for load currents varying from a few milliamperes to motor starting applications with inrush currents as high as 500 amp. Multipole operation is easily achieved with additional silicon controlled rectifiers. A single turnoff circuit can be used to deactuate several poles simultaneously for single throw operations.

Static Circuit Breaker Design

A simplified block diagram of a static circuit breaker is shown in Fig. 11 and consists of a static contact, a load current sensing circuit, an integrating network which determines the time-over-current product, and a level sensitive deactuator circuit. When the

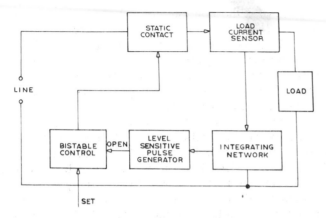

Fig. 11. Block diagram of basic static circuit breaker.

time-current product exceeds the amount specified by the integrating network-pulse generator combination, the pulse generator fires, tripping a bistable control circuit which, in turn, opens the static contact. This type of contactor is set in the closed position by a simple external trigger or pulse in accordance with the specific application, and the characteristic of the control signal and operation is "trip-free." It is anticipated that for a-c circuit breakers, a simple current transformer will be used whose output is rectified and integrated by R_1-C_1 as shown in Figure 12. The energy is stored in capacitor C_1 until it builds up beyond the value specified by the unijunction circuit Q_1, at which time a pulse is generated, tripping the bistable control circuit.

The time-current characteristics are defined by the integrating network R_1-C_1 and the trip point of the unijunction transistor Q_1.

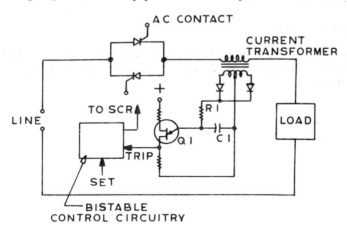

Fig. 12. Simplified circuit diagram of static circuit breaker.

The d-c supplies for the bistable control circuit and transistor Q_1 are derived by a simple transformer rectifier operating off the the line, and the time-current characteristics may be shaped to any desired function by an amplitude shaping network operating on the output of the current transformer. Temperature compensation can be achieved with a thermistor to modify R_1. It may be desirable, under certain conditions of high current, to bypass the resistor R_1 to create immediate trip capability upon overcurrent, and it is anticipated that this type of circuit can be designed for operation on rupture or high overload current to trip within one-half cycle for a-c applications or within 100 microseconds in the case of a d-c contactor. This fast trip capability under short circuit is a primary advantage of the static design, and the fast tripping characteristics can be utilized to prohibit the build-up of current from a generator or other source of electrical power. The bistable control circuit can be a very simple Eccles-Jordan multivibrator which, in turn, actuates the relay circuit. These circuits are of the "trip-free" type and permit reset after overload is removed.

It may be desired to reset automatically the circuit breaker after a specified period of time, and this may be accomplished by inserting a timing circuit in the bistable control circuit. It may also be desired to have the relay reset a specified number of times rather than at a specified rate, and this may be accomplished with a counting circuit such as is common in computer and information handling design. As an additional alternative, it may be desirable to reset the circuit breaker automatically when the overload has cleared, and this can be done by inserting a bridge type of measuring circuit which senses the load impedance when the contact is opened.

Acknowledgment

Much of the work described herein has been for USASRDL, Fort Monmouth. Robert Langfelder developed many of the circuits described.

15. Tunnel Diodes as Amplifiers and Switches

ERICH GOTTLIEB and T. P. SYLVAN

Semiconductor Products Department
General Electric Company
Syracuse, New York

Fast, inexpensive, resistant to nuclear radiation, and having low noise capabilities, the tunnel diode is a new semiconductor device presently challenging the imagination of the electronics industry. This device, judiciously put to use, can reduce equipment size, weight, complexity, and cost while improving performance and reliability.

Device Characteristics

The tunnel diode, so-called because of its use of the quantum mechanical tunneling principle is inherently a negative conductance device. As such, it is particularly well-suited for operation as a sine-wave or relaxation oscillator. Its unique "S" characteristics make it extremely useful for current sensing, current reference, and as both the active and memory switching element in computer circuitry. Due to its region of relatively linear negative conductance, it can also be used as an amplifier. In general, its inherent high speed, resistance to nuclear radiation, low operating power requirements, and wide operating temperature range can make it a valuable asset in a large variety of applications.

A typical tunnel diode is mounted on a standard TO-18 transistor header directly between two of the lead posts. Contact to the top of the diode is made by a thin strip running between the tops of the two lead posts. This structure offers the advantage of a minimum inductance in a single-ended package, since the two

This chapter appeared in the May 1960 issue of Electronic Equipment Engineering and is published here by special arrangement.

leads connected to the top strip can be paralleled to reduce the series inductance. Another significant advantage of this structure is its mechanical strength. This is extremely important in the case of low current, low capacitance diodes where the diameter of the junction can be extremely small. For example, a high performance diode with a peak current of 1 ma will have a diameter of less than 3×10^{-4} inch.

The voltage-current characteristic of a germanium tunnel diode is shown in Fig. 1 together with the important d-c parameters. The dotted line in this figure shows a normal diode characteristic resulting from minority carrier current. It is seen that the tunnel diode follows this characteristic beyond Point C. In the lower voltage region below Point C and in the reverse biased state the diode

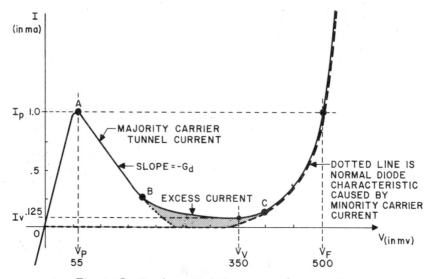

Fig. 1. Static characteristic curve of germanium tunnel diode.

current consists of majority carriers which tunnel through the narrow PN junction with the speed of light. The speed of the quantum mechanical tunneling gives the device its high-frequency capabilities as compared to conventional diodes and transistors which rely on the relatively slow phenomena of drift or diffusion for their operation.

A relatively linear negative conductance region exists between Point A (the peak point) and Point B in Fig. 1. Between Point B and Point C the current is greater than the sum of the theoretical majority and minority currents. The current in this region, identified as the excess current, cannot, as yet, be completely explained. Intuitively the excess current or valley current should be low and therefore the highest peak-point-to-valley-point current ratio seems desirable. There are some tangible reasons for this also.

The greater this ratio, for any given value of peak point current, the greater will be the available output current swing. For example, a tunnel diode with a peak current of 1 ma and a peak-to-valley current ratio of 8 will have an available current swing of 1.0 - 0.125 = 0.875 ma. The peak current of a tunnel diode can be chosen at will and held to within tight limits. Germanium tunnel diodes have been made with peak currents between 100 µa and 10 amp and tolerances on peak current can be maintained to within 10 percent or better on a production basis. However, the peak voltage V_p, valley voltage V_v, and forward voltage V_f are determined by the semiconductor material and are largely fixed. For germanium these voltages are respectively 55 mv, 350 mv, and 500

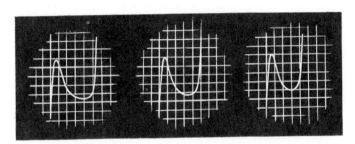

Fig. 2. Voltage-current characteristic curves of typical germanium tunnel diode for ambient temperatures of (left to right) -50 C, +25 C, and +100 C.

mv typical at 25 C. For silicon, the voltages are 75 mv, 450 mv, and 750 mv, while for the recently announced gallium arsenide units the voltages are 150 mv, 500 mv, and 1200 mv. Higher voltages offer the advantage of wider dynamic range and higher output power for applications where these are important.

The magnitude of the negative conductance is equal to the slope di/dv of the voltage current characteristic. For a 1-ma germanium tunnel diode the negative conductance is between 0.006 and 0.010 mho corresponding to a negative resistance between 100 ohms and 160 ohms. If tunnel diodes are to be used in linear amplifiers, the value of the negative conductance must be closely controlled.

Temperature Characteristics

Variation of the tunnel diode parameters with temperature is a matter of extreme importance to the circuit designer. Figure 2 shows the voltage-current characteristic of a typical germanium tunnel diode at temperatures of -55 C, 25 C, and 100 C. Note that the peak voltage, valley voltage, and forward voltage all decrease with increasing temperature while the valley current increases with increasing temperature. The peak current may increase or decrease with temperature depending on the doping agents and the resistivity of the semiconductor material. For the diode shown in Fig. 2, the peak current is a maximum at approximately 25 C and decreases at higher and lower temperatures.

Each application generally has a different temperature problem. For example, in switching circuits the primary concern is the stability of the peak current since it determines the switching threshold, although the changing forward voltage can affect the amplitude of the output voltage.

In oscillators where matching is not required, it may be important only to make sure that at the lowest operating temperatures the device is driven from a voltage source which requires that the resistance of the source supplying the voltage to the tunnel diode is much less than the negative resistance of the diode. Oscillators have been operated successfully over a temperature range from 4 K to over 573 C, a remarkably wide operating range. In amplifiers where some degree of matching between the diode conductance and the circuit conductance is required, this match must be maintained over the required operating temperature range. Stable amplification can be achieved by using either negative feedback or direct temperature compensation with thermistors or other temperature sensitive devices.

The variation of the important d-c parameters between -50 C and 100 C is shown in Fig. 3 for a 1-ma germanium tunnel diode. Note that the peak point voltage has a temperature coefficient of -0.08 millivolts/deg C and the forward voltage has a temperature coefficient of -1.0 millivolts/deg C as compared with a value of -2.5 millivolts/deg C for the forward drop of a conventional diode or transistor.

Frequency Limitations

The small signal equivalent circuit for the tunnel diode when biased in the negative conductance region is shown in Fig. 4. The inductance L_s in the equivalent circuit is relatively low and is determined primarily by the inductance of the leads. A small amount of series resistance R_s is also present which is determined by the bulk resistance of the semiconductor material. The capacitance C is primarily due to the capacitance of the junction although a small portion of the capacitance is due to the leads and the package. The negative conductance $-G_d$ in the equivalent circuit is equal to the slope of the voltage-current characteristic at the particular bias point under consideration. The value of the negative conductance can be assumed to be independent of frequency, the chief limitations in the frequency response of the tunnel diode being determined by the parasitic elements in the equivalent circuit (R_s, L_s, C).

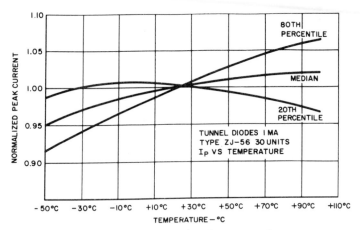

Fig. 3A. Curves showing normalized peak current vs. temperature for tunnel diode Type ZJ-56.

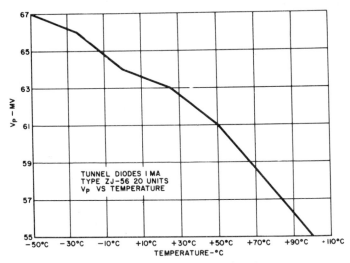

Fig. 3B. Curve showing peak point voltage vs. temperature for tunnel diode Type ZJ-56.

Two significant frequency figures of merit can be assigned to the tunnel diode

(a) resistive cut-off frequency

$$f_{go} = \frac{|G_d|}{2\pi C} \sqrt{\frac{1}{R_s |G_d|} - 1}$$

(b) self-resonant frequency

$$f_o = \frac{1}{2\pi} \sqrt{\frac{1}{L_s C} - \left(\frac{G_d}{C}\right)^{-2}}$$

Both of these frequencies are derived from the equivalent circuit

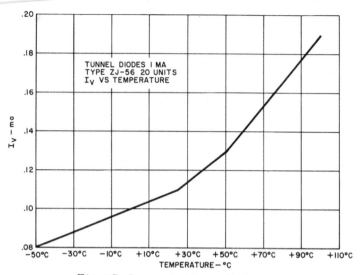

Fig. 3C. Curve showing valley point
current vs. temperature for tunnel
diode Type ZJ-56.

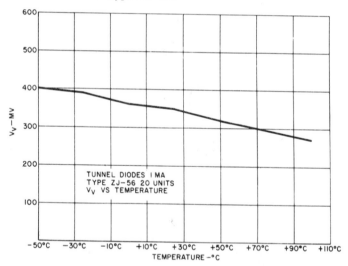

Fig. 3D. Curve showing valley point
voltage vs. temperature for tunnel
diode Type ZJ-56.

of Fig. 4. The resistive cut-off frequency is the frequency at which
the real part of the diode admittance measured at its terminals
goes to zero. The tunnel diode cannot amplify above this frequency.
The self-resonant frequency is the frequency at which the imagi-
nary part of the diode admittance goes to zero. Both frequencies
are reduced by external circuit components and therefore the highest possible operating frequency is very circuit dependent. In a

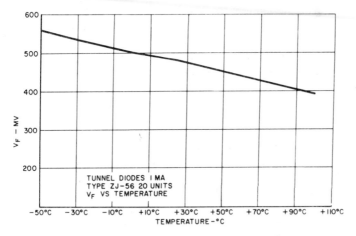

Fig. 3E. Curve showing forward voltage vs. temperature for tunnel diode Type ZJ-56.

transistor package the tunnel diode is limited to frequencies below 1 kmc, this limit being due primarily to the lead inductance. Microstrip or microwave packaging, owing to its inherently lower inductance, can raise the frequency capabilities by an order of magnitude or more.

Noise Performance

In the tunnel diode, one of the major contributions to noise is shot noise. The noise figure in a correctly designed amplifier can be in the range of 3 or 4 db provided that the source conductance is matched to the negative conductance of the tunnel diode. The noise

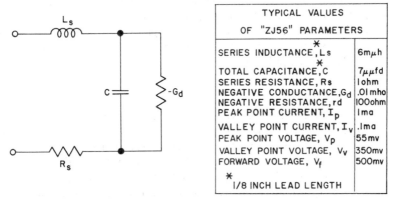

TYPICAL VALUES	
OF "ZJ56" PARAMETERS	
SERIES INDUCTANCE, L_s *	6mμh
TOTAL CAPACITANCE, C *	7$\mu\mu$fd
SERIES RESISTANCE, R_s	1 ohm
NEGATIVE CONDUCTANCE, G_d	.01 mho
NEGATIVE RESISTANCE, rd	100ohm
PEAK POINT CURRENT, I_p	1 ma
VALLEY POINT CURRENT, I_v	.1ma
PEAK POINT VOLTAGE, V_p	55mv
VALLEY POINT VOLTAGE, V_v	350mv
FORWARD VOLTAGE, V_f	500mv
* 1/8 INCH LEAD LENGTH	

Fig. 4. Small signal equivalent circuit and typical values of parameters.

figure is also dependent on the load conductance which might be a mixer or converter stage and be relatively noisy. It is possible, however, to connect the tunnel diode in parallel with the input of a VHF stage and obtain both reduced noise and increased gain. The noise figure is given by the equation:

$$\text{N.F.} = 1 + \frac{20\, I_{dc}}{G_g} + \frac{T_1 \cdot G_1}{T_g \cdot G_g}$$

where I_{dc} is the d-c bias current through the tunnel diode, G_g and G_1 are the conductances of the generator and load, and T_g and T_1 are the effective noise temperatures of the generator and load. From this equation it can be seen that it is desirable to make G_g large and G_1 small. To achieve high gain it is necessary that $G_g + G_1$ be very nearly equal to the conductance of the diode G_d. Thus, to minimize the noise figure it is desirable to make G_g very nearly equal to G_d. The value of I_{dc} should be chosen as low as possible, consistent with a reasonable value of G_d. To satisfy this require-ment, tunnel diodes with high values of peak current to valley cur-rent ratios are desirable.

Nuclear Radiation Effects

Encouraging results have been obtained from preliminary in-vestigations of the effects of nuclear radiation on the character-istics of tunnel diodes. Under a dosage of 3×10^{14} NVT (90 per-cent thermal, 10 percent fast), no apparent change in the electrical characteristics were observed except for the noise figure which increased by approximately 20 percent at the point of maximum negative conductance and by 100 percent near the valley peak.

At a dosage of 5×10^{15} NVT, the valley current increased by about 25 percent while the other d-c characteristics had not changed. The noise figure increased by a factor of 3 at the point of maximum negative conductance while the noise figure in the vicinity of the valley point was immeasurably high. In general, the radiation resistance of tunnel diodes appears to be considerably higher than some tubes or transistors and should be of definite value for military applications.

Linear Amplifiers

On examination of the voltage-current characteristics of the tunnel diode as shown in Figs. 1 and 2, it is evident that for ampli-fier circuits the bias must be supplied from a voltage source to sustain a stable operating point. The bias point should be located near the center of the negative conductance region provided that the noise performance is not at a premium. Biasing at the center of the negative conductance region allows the greatest possible dynamic range to be achieved.

The greatest problem in biasing tunnel diodes is due to the fact that the negative conductance region is not perfectly linear. In amplifier circuits it is necessary to match the diode conductance closely to the circuit conductance if high gain is to be achieved. Slight variations in bias point with the consequent variations in diode conductance can cause large changes in circuit gain. Hence, it is important to ensure a very stable bias voltage. Some of the possible methods for obtaining stable, low impedance supply voltages are (1) use of mercury cells, (2) use of negative feedback, and (3) use of forward biased diodes as voltage regulators.

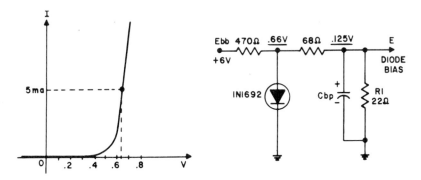

Fig. 5. Silicon diode used as regulator for bias supply.

An example of the use of forward biased diodes for bias stabilization is shown in Fig. 5. Here an inexpensive silicon diode is biased heavily in the forward direction so that it exhibits a low voltage and a low dynamic resistance. A low impedance voltage divider is used to reduce the diode voltage to the value desired for biasing of the tunnel diode.

A graphical analysis of the operation of a parallel amplifier stage is shown in Fig. 6. The voltage-current characteristic of the tunnel diode is represented by Curve 1, the net circuit conductance is represented by Curve 2, and the resultant input characteristic of the over-all amplifier stage is represented by Curve 3. The slope of the input characteristic in the active region (between A'' and B'') is close to horizontal indicating a high input impedance. The value of the input impedance is given by

$$Z_{in} = \frac{1}{G_T} = \frac{1}{G_g + G_l - G_d}$$

and the available power gain would be given by

$$PG_{av} = \frac{4G_g G_l}{G_T^2}$$

It can be seen both graphically and mathematically that to obtain a

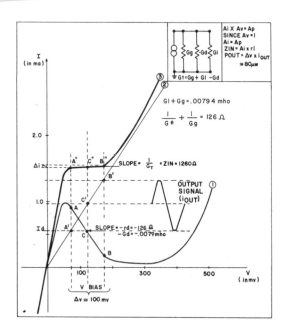

Fig. 6. Graphical analysis of parallel amplifier stage.

high value of available power gain it is necessary for Z_{in} to be very large and positive. This requires $G_g + G_l$ to be very nearly equal to but larger than G_d. Since the voltage is the same across all the conductances in the circuit, the voltage gain of the parallel circuit will be unity.

The closer $G_g + G_l$ is to G_d, the greater is the current amplifi-

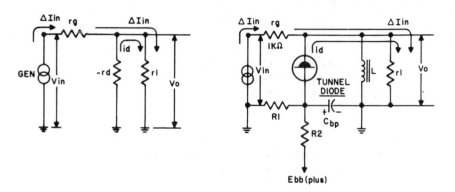

Fig. 7. Parallel amplifier stage and equivalent circuit.

cation obtained. A similar graphical analysis can be applied to the series connection resulting in a "low" input impedance circuit and voltage gain.

Figure 7 shows an audio amplifier circuit yielding about 30 db gain. It is much more difficult to build a low frequency amplifier circuit, incidentally, since the tunnel diode is inherently trying to oscillate at a very high frequency. The use of audio components and audio type layouts, generally result in enough stray inductance to enable the circuit to oscillate freely at high frequencies since bypassing is not a simple matter in the UHF range. Additional circuit stability criteria therefore are:

1. f_o of the circuit to be equal or above f_{go} to avoid self-oscillations.
2. The sum of the load and generator conductances must be nearly equal to, but always greater than the negative conductance of the diode (in the parallel type circuit).
3. The total d-c loop conductance must be larger than the negative conductance (voltage source).
4. All above requirements must remain satisfied over a range of supply voltages and temperature conditions.

Amplifier circuits have been built anywhere from audio frequencies up to 225 Mc yielding gains in the 30 db range with excellent bandwidth. As an example a 100-Mc circuit was built having 32-db gain with a bandwidth of 20 Mc.

Switching Circuits

One of the most promising areas for the application of tunnel diodes is in switching circuits, particularly in large scale computers where the tunnel diode can economically perform both the logic and memory functions. Here the tunnel diode offers the advantages of small size, low operating power, high speed, potential low cost, and high reliability.

It is possible to form a simple bistable circuit by connecting a tunnel diode in series with a voltage source and a single resistor. For bistable operation it is only necessary that the load line formed by the voltage source and resistor intersect the diode characteristic curve of Figs. 1 and 2 at two points where the characteristic curve has a positive slope. These two points represent the two stable states of the circuit. If a larger series resistance is used, the diode can be considered to be biased from a constant current source. A constant current bistable load line would be represented in Fig. 1 or 2 by a horizontal line lying between the peak point and the valley point. As an example, consider a constant current load line of 0.7 ma in Fig. 1. The diode would have approximately 30 millivolts across it in the ON state and approximately

470 millivolts across it in the OFF state. In the ON state the current through the diode consists entirely of majority carriers transported across the junction by the tunneling mechanism, while in the OFF state the current through the diode consists entirely of minority carriers transported across the junction by diffusion.

The diode can be triggered from the ON state to the OFF state by means of a current pulse which temporarily increases the current through the diode to a value greater than the peak current. Similarly the diode can be triggered from the OFF state to the ON state by means of a current pulse which temporarily reduces the current through the diode to a value less than the valley current. The switching speed is very high and is determined chiefly by the junction capacity and the amount of charge available from the triggering pulse. If a constant current load line is used with a trigger of minimum amplitude, the rise time of the voltage across the diode between the 10 percent and 90 percent points will be given approximately by

$$t_r = \left(\frac{V_f - V_p}{I_p - I_v} \right) C$$

Using the typical parameters for the ZJ56 listed in Fig. 4, the rise time is calculated as 3.5 mμs, which is in close agreement with measured values. Since V_f, V_p, and $C/(I_p - I_v)$ are largely independent of I_p, the rise time will also be independent of I_p. The rise time can be decreased by reducing the ratio $C/(I_p - I_v)$ or the ratio of C/G_d. Switching speeds of less than 1 mμs have been measured for 10 ma versions of the ZJ56.

The voltage of the germanium tunnel diode in the OFF state V_f is approximately 0.5 volt which is considerably higher than the base-to-emitter voltage of a germanium alloy transistor (approximately 0.3 volt with a base current of 1 ma). Accordingly, it is possible to switch a PNP or NPN germanium alloy transistor directly with the output from a germanium tunnel diode. This permits the tunnel diode to be used in conjunction with conventional transistors to form many useful types of switching circuits. One example is the simple flip-flop circuit shown in Fig. 8. In this circuit a current which is lower than the peak current is supplied by the 6800-ohm resistor. When the tunnel diode is ON a low voltage exists at the base of the transistor and the transistor will be off. If a positive pulse occurs at the input, the current through the tunnel diode increases above the peak current and the tunnel diode switches to the high voltage state. The tunnel diode will remain in the high voltage state and the major portion of the current from the 6800-ohm resistor will be diverted into the base of the transistor causing it to turn on and the voltage at its collector will fall to a very low value. Similarly, a negative pulse at the input will cause the current in the tunnel diode to drop below the valley current and

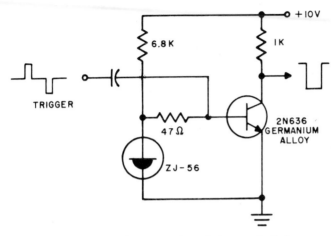

Fig. 8. Bistable circuit using tunnel diode and NPN germanium alloy transistor.

cause the tunnel diode to switch to its low voltage state which in turn will cause the transistor to turn off. The 47-ohm resistor serves to bias the tunnel diode above the valley point voltage when it is in its OFF state and also serves to prevent the tunnel diode from loading the trigger pulse thus increasing the switching speed of the transistor.

The time delay circuit shown in Fig. 9 permits any number of consecutive time delays to be obtained with relatively simple circuitry. The timing cycle is initiated by applying a step voltage of +10 volts at the input. The capacitor C_1 is charged through the 3300-ohm resistor and the current through the first tunnel diode increases in proportion to the voltage on C_1. When the current

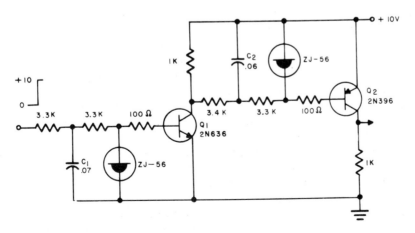

Fig. 9. Tunnel diode time delay circuit with two cascaded complementary stages.

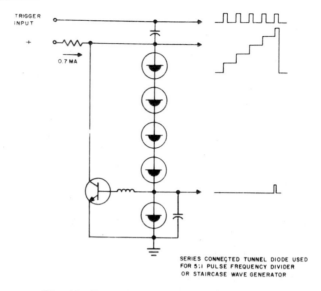

Fig. 10. Series connected tunnel diodes used for 5-to-1 pulse frequency divider or staircase wave generator.

through the tunnel diode increases to the peak current, the tunnel diode will switch to its high voltage state and cause Q1 to turn on. The voltage at the collector of Q1 will then fall from +10 volts to a low value and a similar timing sequence will be initiated for the second stage. The second stage is a complementary version of the first stage. At the end of the second timing sequence, Q2 will turn on and the voltage at its collector will rise from zero to +10 volts. For the circuit shown each time delay is approximately 100 μsec. A multiple phase oscillator can be obtained by connecting an odd number of stages in a closed loop.

A simple 5 to 1 pulse frequency divider is shown in Fig. 10. Here, five tunnel diodes are connected in series and are biased from a current source which has a lower value than the peak current of any of the diodes. The bottom diode is selected to have a higher peak current than any of the other diodes in the circuit. Each time a positive pulse occurs at the input, one diode is switched from its low-voltage state to its high-voltage state. When the fifth pulse occurs, the bottom diode is switched to its high-voltage state and turns on the NPN transistor which resets the circuit by diverting the current from the tunnel diodes and causing them all to revert to their low-voltage state. The capacitor across the bottom diode and the inductance in series with the base of the transistor serve to delay the signal to the transistor so that complete switching can occur. The waveform appearing across the tunnel diodes is a staircase with a risetime determined by the risetime of the

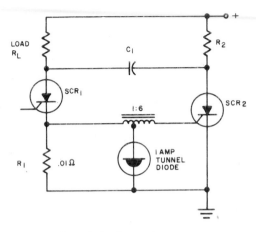

Fig. 11. Tunnel diode used as current sensing element in silicon controlled rectifier
circuit breaker.

trigger pulse. The operating frequency is limited chiefly by the
switching speed of the reset transistor. A circuit using an avalanche transistor has been built which can perform the reset function in approximately 2 mμs.

The tunnel diode has many applications in current sensing and
current limiting circuits for power equipment. An example of the
use of a high current tunnel diode as the reference element in a
silicon controlled rectifier circuit breaker is shown in Fig. 11.

When the load current increases above the limiting value, the
voltage across the 0.01-ohm current-sensing resistor will exceed
the peak point voltage and cause the tunnel diode to switch to its
high-voltage state. The voltage swing of the tunnel diode will be
stepped up by the autotransformer to a value which is high enough
to fire the silicon controlled rectifier SCR2. When SCR2 fires, a
negative voltage is coupled to SCR1 by the capacitor Cp which
causes SCR1 to turn off and interrupt the load current in 20 μsec
or less. The chief advantage offered by the tunnel diode in this
application is its ability to be triggered at a very low voltage level.
This in turn results in a very low power loss in the current monitoring resistor.

16. Asymmetrical Slaving Circuit for AC Power Switching

D. L. WATROUS and J. D. HARNDEN, Jr.

General Engineering Laboratory
General Electric Company
Schenectady, New York

The concept of the multijunction semiconductor has been receiving considerable attention lately. The PNPN structure is perhaps the oldest of these. (1,2) These devices offer outstanding characteristics for switching applications because of their near perfect characteristics, stability, high gain, and potentially low manufacturing cost. Both two- and three-terminal devices are commercially available with multiterminal units receiving considerable development attention.

The commerically available silicon controlled rectifier is one of the most important varieties. (3,4) A variety of units is available, with current ratings from a fraction of an ampere to about 100 amperes, and peak voltage ratings in some cases as high as 400 volts. There is often a marked similarity in appearance between controlled rectifiers and ordinary rectifiers, and often similar specifications apply. The silicon controlled rectifier makes available for the first time a practical solid-state device analogous to the familiar thyratron. The use of this component circumvents some of the problems normally associated with transistor circuits such as restricted voltages, power and current ratings, and allows utilization of many of the important thyratron circuit concepts previously developed. While the concept of a solid-state switching device is not new, the availability of reproducible high power units is an innovation. From an application viewpoint, the approximately equal forward and reverse voltage

174

rating is of considerable importance. The controlled rectifier is a silicon device using some of the properties of transistors and rectifiers. The unit can be produced economically in large volume.

The controlled rectifier has a minimum power gain in excess of 150,000. On the basis of pulsed input, the power gain is much greater. The device has a deionization time considerably shorter than that of thyratrons under most operating conditions. When conducting, the forward voltage drop is about 20 percent greater than for the equivalent silicon rectifier and drastically lower than the 12 to 15-volt drop in thyratrons. Peak voltage ratings in excess of 400 volts are presently available with higher voltage designs paralleling advancements in normal rectifier P.I.V. ratings and packaging techniques. The allowable current depends on the junction area, method and effectiveness of cooling, and current waveform. Water cooling offers a medium for considerably extending the allowable current per junction as with any rectifier. Available I^2t data indicates that proper fusing can be selected. Parallel, series, and multiphase connections offer considerable flexibility in application.

The controlled rectifier can be applied in a wide variety of equipment including inverters, converters, power supplies, motor controls, etc. Another broad area is that of static switching. Since the controlled rectifier is small, efficient, ultrafast, non-wearing, potentially inexpensive, and capable of precise control, many new concepts in static switching techniques should be possible. These will involve both a-c and d-c power sources. This chapter is restricted to a-c power supplies in the sense that commutation methods are not considered. However, the slaving technique described can be applied in d-c circuitry with somewhat different operating characteristics.

Basic Slaving Circuits

In a-c switching it is often desirable to have a single controlled rectifier initiate the action involving several other units. The type of slaving described is most applicable to contactor-like operation, wherein the conduction is either 0 or a full cycle.

A preliminary circuit is shown in Fig. 1. In this case an attempt is made to fire SCR-2 after the operation of SCR-1 during the previous half cycle. Thus, the current transformer capacitor-storage system indicated was examined. The firing of SCR-1 is a result of the flow of gate current through R1 as a matter of convenience. There are several shortcomings associated with this circuit, including the excessively large value of C, which the basic circuit of Fig. 2 overcomes.

In Fig. 2 two SCR's are connected in parallel to form an a-c switch that controls power to the load. As a matter of convenience

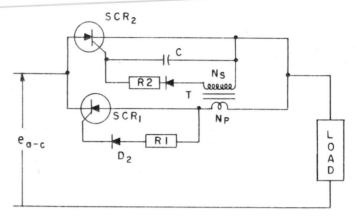

Fig. 1. Capacitor storage slaving circuit.

SCR-1 is triggered by gate current flowing through R, when line 1 is positive. The function of the slaving circuit consisting of the transformer and diode D2 is to fire SCR-2 at the beginning of the next negative half cycle. In this particular circuit the transformer is designed as a current transformer, which implies that the primary voltage rating is negligible compared to the load voltage. Under these conditions the maximum secondary voltage occurs when the primary current goes through zero. Increasing conduction current in SCR-1 drives the transformer flux towards positive saturation. As this current decreases, the induced secondary voltage is of the proper polarity to be clamped by diode D2 and the gate-cathode junction of SCR-2. By limiting the induced secondary voltage, the rate of flux reset in the transformer is also limited. As a result, the inductively stored energy is carried over into the negative half cycle causing SCR-2 to conduct when its cathode goes negative. Several biasing techniques can be used to provide greater flexibility and multiple controlled techniques.

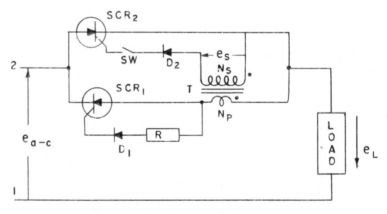

Fig. 2. Basic inductive slaving circuit.

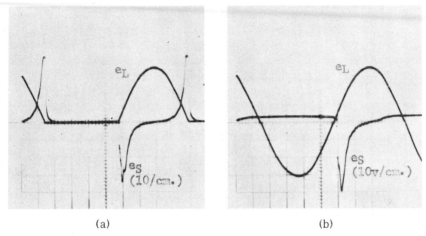

(a)   (b)

Fig. 3. Waveforms for basic circuit of Fig. 2. The
time scale is 2 milliseconds per division.

The waveforms in Fig. 3a show a comparison, for the circuit
of Fig. 2, of the half-wave sinusoidal load voltage with the secondary transformer voltage when the switch is open. In Fig. 3b the
same waveforms are shown with the switch closed. Here the positive gate pulse has been commutated into the negative half cycle
causing SCR-2 to conduct. The amount of carry-over is a matter
of design. In some cases it might only be necessary to carry over
sufficient firing power for the first few degrees of the negative
half cycle. Since the SCR-2 gate voltage lasts for the entire negative half cycle, it would be possible to operate with lighter loads
or reduce the size of the transformer. The transformer used for
these tests was wound on one of the smallest available split C
cores, with a small air gap in each leg. The primary consists of
three turns, and the secondary had 800 turns. In other designs and
with different load conditions a single turn could be used for the
primary.

The circuit shown in Fig. 4 uses a similar slaving circuit, except the transformer is excited from the load voltage, rather than
current. The primary is designed to operate with a smaller current and is connected in series with a large resistance R2 to
limit the maximum current. The core is identical with that used in
Fig. 2, but the primary turns are now equal to the secondary turns
(800). Again as a matter of convenience R1 is used to fire the gate
of SCR-1.

The waveforms for this circuit are shown in Fig. 5. In Fig. 5a
the half-wave sinusoidal load voltage and the transformer primary
current are compared. The primary current was measured as a
voltage drop across the series resistance R2. In Fig. 5b the comparison is between the transformer primary current and voltage,

again using the voltage across R2 when SW-1 is open. In Fig. 5c the transformer primary current can be compared with the primary voltage when SW-1 is closed. Here SCR-2 fires from the commutated pulse. Figures 5d and 5e show examples of symmetrical and asymmetrical operation. To obtain these waveforms SW-2 is switched to the external signal position. A 20-cps source was used for this signal, thus producing an a-c load pulse every third cycle. When SCR-1 is triggered at the beginning of the half cycle, a complete symmetrical output voltage pulse results as

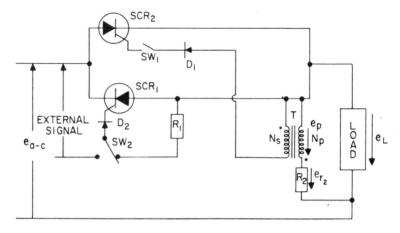

Fig. 4. Basic circuit using load voltage.

shown in Fig. 5d. As the firing of SCR-1 is delayed the output becomes asymmetrical as shown in Fig. 5e. Even though the positive conduction period is relatively short, sufficient firing power is carried over through zero into the negative half cycle to properly trigger SCR-2.

Transformer Design

The design of the slaving transformer is a function of (1) the minimum primary current required to insure sufficient flux change to fire, (2) the maximum heating determined by the rms primary current, and (3) the maximum power required to fire the slaved SCR. To insure that the slaved SCR will fire, sufficient voltage and current must be provided. The flux reset volt-seconds must provide the firing voltage for more than 1/4 cycle of the supply frequency to insure sufficient carry-over into the next half cycle. The secondary current must exceed the required SCR gate current. In practice, the secondary voltage may need to be as large as 5 volts to adequately fire the least sensitive SCR's, allowing some margin for forward voltage drops in series diodes.

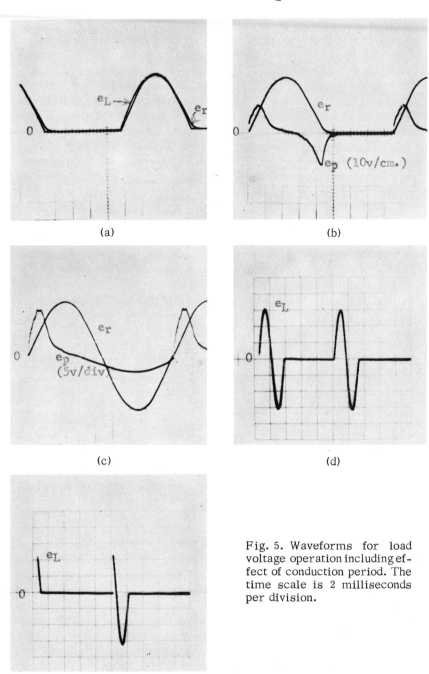

(a)

(b)

(c)

(d)

(e)

Fig. 5. Waveforms for load voltage operation including effect of conduction period. The time scale is 2 milliseconds per division.

Multifunction Operation

These techniques are applicable to a wide variety of circuits including full-wave rectified, polyphase, d-c, sequence, and lock-in circuits wherein only one gate is controlled and full conduction takes place for all other SCR's. There will be either 180 degrees or zero negative conduction regardless of the extent of the positive conduction. In some cases therefore, inrush currents can more easily be controlled as compared to indiscriminately closing during any portion of the cycle as with relay contacts. Radio interference is also minimized as compared to phase control since no sharp wave fronts are involved.

Regenerative Inductive Slaving

The inductive slaving techniques described previously may be extended to yield a regenerative slaving operation between SCR's. By cross coupling two SCR's and two slaving transformers, each SCR can be made to fire only if the alternate SCR conducted in

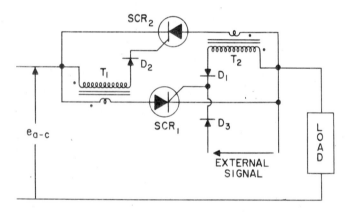

Fig. 6. Basic regeneration circuit.

the preceding half cycle. Figure 6 shows a circuit employing this scheme. The components used in the tests are the same as described for Fig. 2.

If SCR-1 is fired during a positive half cycle, T1 will cause SCR-2 to conduct during the negative half cycle. Transformer T2 will refire SCR-1, producing the next positive half cycle. Thus, once SCR-1 is fired, no further external signal is required to keep both SCR's conducting during their respective half cycles. To stop the regenerative action it is necessary to interrupt one of the gating signals. This configuration of SCR's is equivalent to a relay employing holding contacts. With the addition of extra components,

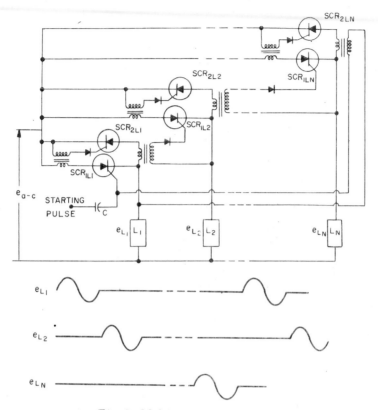

Fig. 7. Multi-unit operation.

a single transformer could be located in the load circuit, but the two transformer circuit is simpler and less expensive.

There are several methods of interrupting the regenerative action and hence, opening up this a-c switch. Some of these methods are:

1. Remove the a-c power.

2. Bias one transformer far into saturation either with a d-c winding or a permanent magnet.

3. Provide sufficient, shorted turns on one transformer so that the core capacitance is reduced below the critical amount for firing.

4. Place a switch in one SCR gate lead. This can be a mechanical contact, a gated diode, a switching transformer, or a saturable reactor.

An interesting "counter" circuit, shown in Fig. 7, indicates the flexibility of the technique. A starting pulse is applied to the gate of SCR-1L1 causing SCR-2L1 to conduct on the next half cycle. The output of the transformer associated with this SCR is applied to the gate of SCR-1L2 causing it to conduct on the next half cycle.

If the output of the last SCR to conduct is connected to the input of SCR-1L1 which started the sequence, the operation will repeat with each pair of SCR's producing an output pulse. Other similar circuits are easy to design. One in particular would involve feeding back as well as forward to pairs of SCR's.

Differential Pulse Operation

A circuit employing one slaving transformer and one switching transistor was built to show feasibility and is shown in Fig. 8. In this circuit, the slaving transformer primary is connected in series with the load. Thus, it senses when either SCR conducts.

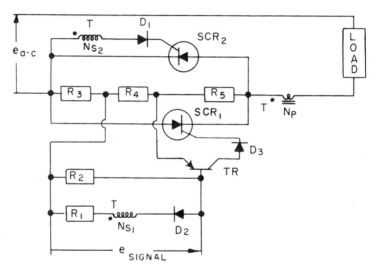

Fig. 8. Simple differential pulse circuit.

Transistor TR is biased OFF by the resistor divider R2, R3, R4, and R5, and hence SCR-1 does not fire. Diode D3 prevents reverse voltage from being applied to the transistor when both SCR's are blocking. If a negative pulse is applied to the transistor base (when SCR-1 is blocking in the forward direction), the transistor will turn ON and fire SCR-1. The transformer will sense that SCR-1 conducted and fire SCR-2 on the alternate half cycle. The transformer also senses that SCR-2 conducted and as a result winding N-S1 applies a negative signal to the transistor base. SCR-1 is refired and the action is regenerative. To stop the regeneration, the transistor N-S1 is pulsed OFF by applying a positive signal to the base. Resistor R1 must be large enough to prevent excessive loading on winding N-S1 and small enough to allow the transistor, base-emitter diode, and diode D2 to commutate the current. In practice, the compromise is not difficult to achieve. For the transistor used in this evaluation approximately 0.5 volt and 500 microamperes will operate the unit for either signal polarity. Successive pulses of a given polarity have no effect on the state of the circuit, since it responds only to the first one, and only of the correct polarity. The output of the circuit is thus zero or an ac with 360-degree conduction.

Conclusions

The circuits described provide a simple, reliable, and inexpensive method of slaving two or more SCR's. Although only 60-cycle operation has been considered, the application of these techniques to other frequencies should follow directly. The specific transformer design will depend on the nature of the load. In general, current transformers will be less expensive than potential transformers. In any event, the cost will be low as a result of the small size. The regenerative techniques allow simulation of holding contact operation. These inductive slaving circuits should be useful in many types of logic, sequencing, counting, and relay applications as a result of their simplicity, reliability, speed, and low cost.

REFERENCES

1. Ebers, J. J., "Four-Terminal PNPN Transistors." IRE Proceedings, Vol. 40, Nov. 1952, pp 1361-1364.
2. Moll, J. L., M. Tanenbaum, J. M. Goldey, and N. Holonyak. "PNPN Transistor Switches." IRE Proceedings, Vol. 44, Sept. 1956, pp 1174-1182.
3. Bisson, D. K., and R. F. Dyer. "A Silicon Controlled Rectifier —Its Characteristics and Rating." AIEE Transactions, 58-1248.
4. Application Notes on the Controlled Rectifier. Semiconductor Products Department, ECC-371-1, General Electric Company.

17. Transistor Sampling Relay

R. DEAN OLSON

Hughes Aircraft Company
Culver City, California

The collector-to-emitter resistance of a transistor in the cutoff state is high—usually many megohms. The collector-to-emitter resistance of the same transistor in the saturated state is only a few ohms. These characteristics are used to develop circuits that are in many ways similar to SPST relays. There are some differences between the operation of these circuits and the operation of mechanical relays. In most cases, these differences are advantages over the mechanical relays. Figure 1 shows a comparison of the voltage-current characteristics of a mechanical relay with the voltage-current characteristics of a transistor in the saturated and cutoff states. The curves show that there is a region in the saturated transistor voltage-current characteristic which corresponds to the mechanical relay voltage-current characteristic in the ON or "pulled in" state. Also, there is a region in the cutoff transistor characteristic which corresponds to the mechanical relay characteristic in the OFF state. For relay operation, the transistors are operated in these linear regions of the curves which correspond quite closely to the mechanical relay characteristics.

When a transistor is operated in the switching mode, it is sometimes helpful to think of the device as a pair of back-to-back diodes rather than as a transistor. This is illustrated in Fig. 2. This analogy does not hold for the conducting or saturated condition of the transistor since transistor action (gain) must take place to obtain conduction from collector to emitter. However, in the cutoff state and the reverse configuration (explained later) the analogy holds true.

The circuit shown in Fig. 3 exhibits the characteristics of a SPST relay for switching single polarity signals. An NPN transistor

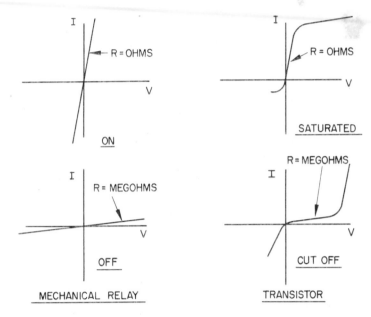

Fig. 1. Comparison between mechanical
relay and transistor characteristics.

is used for switching positive signals and a PNP transistor for
negative signals. To prevent the control voltage from summing with
or degrading the switched signal, the control circuit must be floating with respect to this signal. Transformer coupling of the control
signal to the relay is therefore used. The necessity for a-c coupling immediately limits this type of relay to relatively short
periods of ON time. For this reason, the relays discussed in this
chapter are called sampling relays. The time during which the relay is "pulled in" is limited only by the ability of the transformer
to supply sufficient current to the base of the transistor to hold it
in saturation.

Operation of the relay is as follows. The signal to be sampled is
a positive signal. With no input to the control transformer, the
transistor is cut off since the base and emitter are at the same potential. The collector-emitter resistance of the transistor is sev-

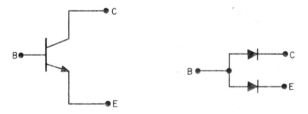

Fig. 2. Transistor-diode analogy.

eral megohms. The signal, therefore, is not transferred to the load. The load must be chosen such that the leakage current of the transistor will develop only a negligible voltage across it. In applications where the load is fixed, transistors with sufficiently small leakage current must be used to obtain the desired degree of isolation. When a current pulse of sufficient magnitude is applied to the base of the transistor through the control transformer, the transistor saturates. The input signal less the drop due to the saturation resistance of the transistor is developed across the load. The saturation resistance typically is less than 200 ohms for silicon transistors. Should this be an appreciable percentage of the load

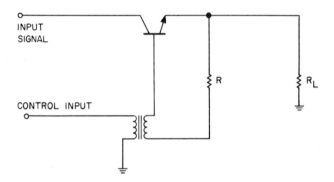

Fig. 3. Single transistor relay.

resistance, certain types of silicon transistors can be used which have saturation resistances of the order of 25 ohms or less. Germanium transistors can have saturation resistances as small as fractions of an ohm.

When a negative signal is applied to the input "contact," the signal will appear across the load regardless of the presence or absence of control voltage if the signal is more negative than the control voltage at the base of the transistor. This is because the signal itself biases the base-collector diode of the transistor in the forward direction. Current will flow through this diode, the transformer winding, and the resistance R to the load R_L. As long as the control pulse is large enough to keep the base more negative than the collector during the "open" time, this relay will switch negative signals. The magnitude of the control pulse is limited, however, by the breakdown voltage of the base-emitter diode which is usually quite small for grown or diffused junction transistors. This in turn limits the magnitude of negative signals that can be switched. Negative signals of large magnitude must be switched by PNP transistors. The fact that this type of relay cannot switch certain types of signals is a serious limitation. A sampling relay which does not have this limitation is shown in Fig. 4.

The theory of operation of this relay is similar to the single transistor relay except that two transistors are used back to back to provide obstruction for both positive and negative signals when the transistors are cut off. The transistors are connected such that a positive pulse at the transformer causes both transistors to saturate. When no pulse is present, both transistors are cut off. A first glance at the back-to-back configuration may lead one to believe that transistors with symmetrical characteristics — interchangeable collector and emitter — would be necessary for proper operation. This actually is not the case. The transistor through which the current is flowing in the reverse direction is really not operating as a transistor. It is more like two back-to-back diodes as shown in Fig. 2. The first diode (base to emitter) is forward biased by the control voltage. The second diode (base to collector) is forward biased by the signal. The signal will appear at the output as long as the control current through the base-emitter diode is sufficient to hold it in the conducting state.

To see how this relay functions, consider first the cutoff state. When a positive voltage is applied to the input collector, the base-collector diode of that transistor is back biased. The base-emitter

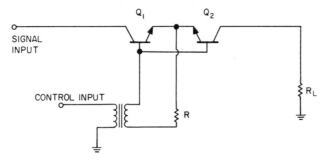

Fig. 4. Two transistor relay.

diodes of both transistors are back biased because of the absence of a control pulse. The signal, therefore, is blocked and the impedance across the "relay contact" is of the order of several megohms. If a negative signal is applied to the input collector, the base-collector diode of the second transistor is back biased as are the base-emitter diodes of both transistors. Again the signal is blocked. Consider now the case where both transistors are saturated due to the presence of an input control pulse. When a positive voltage is applied, the resistance across the first transistor is the transistor saturation resistance. Both diodes of the second transistor are forward biased, the base-emitter diode by the control voltage and the base-collector diode by the signal. Therefore, the input voltage less the drop due to the transistor saturation resistance appears at the output. In the case of a negative voltage applied to the input collector, the same argument applies except that the roles of the two transistors are exactly reversed. The relay switches positive and negative signals equally well. Alternating current signals are switched with no degradation of the wave form.

Many factors govern the speed of response of this type of relay. The particular application will dictate the type of transformer and transistor which must be used to obtain proper results. The transformer must be able to supply current to the bases of the transistors for the required period of "hold-in" time. It must also be able to pass the leading and trailing edges of the "pull-in" pulse sufficiently rapid to meet specifications of "pull-in" and "drop-out" times. The parameters to be considered for the transistor are low saturation resistance for low "closed" resistance, very low leakage current for high "open" resistance, high voltage breakdown for switching large signals, and short rise time, storage time, and fall time for speed of response and high sampling rates. Rise time, storage time, and fall time are three terms which are not normally associated with relay circuits. In fast acting transistor relay circuits they must be considered. Rise time is defined as the time necessary for the signal to rise to 90 percent of its final value across the load. Storage time is the time between removal of the control pulse and the start of the decay of the signal across the load. Fall time is the time necessary for the signal to decay to 10 percent of its full value across the load. Any one type of transistor cannot meet all of these requirements in the best manner possible. It is necessary to match the transistor to the application.

In one circuit Type 2N497 transistors were used. Pull-in time for this relay was in the order of 1-to-2 microseconds. Storage time was approximately 5 microseconds and the fall time was about 3 microseconds. A 50-volt signal was being switched to a 10,000-ohm load when these measurements were taken. The "open" resistance of this relay was measured to be well over 100 megohms and the "closed" resistance was less than 20 ohms. Switching rates up to 25 kc are possible with this type of transistor. For applications where sampling rates must be higher, some of the newer types of transistors can be used with excellent results.

The Type 2N1254 to 2N1259 series of Hughes silicon double diffused mesa transistors, for example, can be used to sample a signal at rates of 100 kc or more. This is due to the low storage time and fast response of this type of transistor. Signals up to 50 volts in magnitude can be switched. The saturation resistance is of the order of 30 ohms. The leakage current is such that the "open" resistance is greater than 50 megohms at room temperature.

In applications where the duty cycle of the control pulse is high, the reverse voltage across the base-emitter diode will become relatively large. The reason for this is the so called "equal area rule," the area below the average value of a voltage wave form

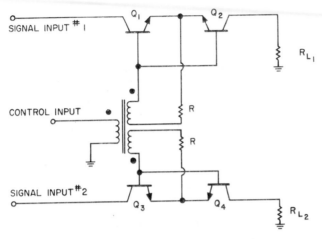

Fig. 5. Double pole-single throw relay.

equals the area above. As the duty cycle increases, the effective
negative swing of the control pulse increases. Care must be taken
to insure that the emitter-base reverse voltage does not exceed the
breakdown potential of the transistor used. Although operation of the
relay is not affected, the life of the transistors may be shortened
and permanent damage may result if the allowable power dissipation
is exceeded.

The transformer input for the control voltage permits this relay
to be used in other configurations. A two-winding secondary on the
transformer can be used to switch two such pairs of back-to-back
transistors to make a DPST relay as shown in Fig. 5. This type of
relay configuration is being used in a time sharing mechanism to
display several symbols on a cathode-ray tube from one gun. The
relays sample each of the vertical and horizontal signals in sequence. The outputs of the relays are summed to form two composite deflection signals. This is but one of many applications where
a sampling relay of this type can be used.

If the ON and OFF times of the sampling relay are more or less
symmetrical, it may be made to operate as a SPDT relay. This is
accomplished by connecting the two output leads together and reversing the leads of one secondary winding on the transformer as
shown in Fig. 6. As the control waveform goes positive, one switch
will allow a signal to pass while the other switch will block the
second signal. When the control voltage goes negative, the switches
reverse states. The first signal is blocked and the second signal
is transferred to the load. The output voltage is switched alternately
between the two input voltages. The control signal can be unsymmetrical as long as it can supply sufficient current to the transistors
to hold them saturated at the proper time.

The basic circuit of this transistor relay can be used in other

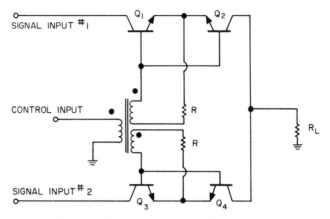

Fig. 6. Single pole-double throw relay.

interesting applications. For proper relay action, the transistors either must be saturated or cut off. Consider, however, the non-saturated region of the transistors. Figure 7 shows a graph of a typical circuit showing the change of effective resistance across the device as the base current into the transistors is increased. The i_b - R_{eff} curve is very linear except near the cutoff and saturation regions. The linearity of this relationship allows the circuit to be used in applications where a resistance proportional to a control current is desired. R. F. Shea, in his book "Transistor Circuit Engineering," gives an interesting application using this principle. Two of these current variable resistors are used in conjunction with other circuitry to form a low level limiter. The circuit diagram is shown in Fig. 8. The current variable resistors are the shunt arms of a voltage divider. The signal itself varies the resistance of the voltage divider to keep the output a constant magnitude. Each of the two shunt arms conducts for one half the time. The control signals to these two shunt arms are 180 degrees

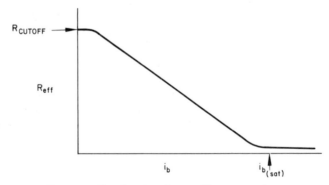

Fig. 7. Graph showing collector-emitter resistance vs. base current.

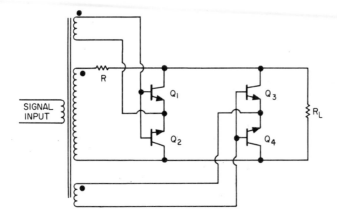

Fig. 8. Low level limiter.

out of phase. Thus, limiting action occurs for both the positive and negative swings of the incoming signal.

Another very useful application of the basic relay circuit is a phase detector as shown in Fig. 9. The reference signal is used as a relay control signal to cut off or saturate the transistors alternately. The signal, therefore, is allowed to pass during the time when the transistors are saturated and is blocked when the transistors are cut off. If the input signal and the reference signal are the same frequency, the d-c output of the filter will be an indication of the phase difference of the two signals.

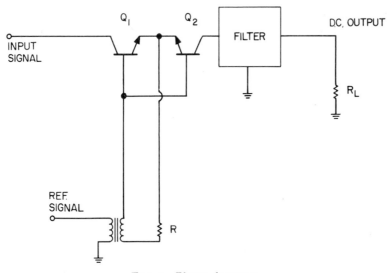

Fig. 9. Phase detector.

Summary

The transistor relay as described here exhibits the characteristics of a SPST relay. It is limited to sampling operation due to
the necessity of a-c coupling the control voltage. Extremely fast
"pull-in" and "drop-out" times can be obtained by proper choice
of transistors. This permits sampling rates up to 100 kc with
presently available transistors. The open resistance of this relay
is several megohms and can be made hundreds of megohms by
proper transistor choice. Closed resistances are less than 200
ohms and can be only a few ohms if certain types of transistors
are used. Circuit requirements will dictate the type of transistor
to be used since no single type is best for all applications. By
combining two of the basic relay circuits, a DPST relay is obtained. A SPDT relay is also possible by proper connection provided the control wave form is more or less symmetrical. The
basic relay circuit can also be used in several ways other than relay applications.

18. The Photoswitch

Texas Instruments, Inc.
Dallas, Texas

Until recently the emphasis has been on transistor switching devices in which high speed and low power are the major considerations. To increase the power handling capabilities of semiconductor switches, 4-layer or PNPN devices have been useful.

For "normal" transistors (if there are such things) the grounded base current gain (α) is less than 1. For many years transistors referred to as "hook" transistors were investigated. The usual configuration of these structures was a PNPN structure usually obtained by accident while fabricating other types. The unusual characteristic of these transistors was the fact that α under appropriate bias conditions was greater than unity and regions of negative resistance were observed. (Not unlike some of the early point contact transistors.) These hook collector transistors were the forerunners of our PNPN switching devices.

The usual PNPN device is characterized by a high impedance OFF state and a low impedance ON state. Switching between these two states is usually accomplished by one of two methods. In the case of a two-terminal device the switching is accomplished by means of application of a voltage in excess of the breakdown voltage of the device. For the three-terminal devices, application of gate current triggers the device from the blocking state to the ON state.

The usual configuration found in a PNPN switch is shown in Fig. 1. When the device is biased with the P emitter positive, junction J_2 will be reverse biased and very little current will flow through the device unless the applied voltage exceeds the avalanche voltage breakdown of junction J_2. With reverse bias (P emitter negative), J_1 and J_3 are reverse biased and very little current flows. Usually J_1 is of low breakdown and J_3 of high reverse breakdown. The current through J_2 consists of holes

193

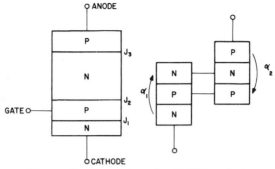

Fig. 1. Configuration of a PNPN switch.

emitted from J_3 and electrons emitted from J_1. In other words, J_2 is the collector of the NPN transistor and the PNP transistor.

If α_1 represents the current gain of the NPN transistor and α_2 represents the current gain of the PNP transistor, it can be shown that when the sum of α_1 and α_2 exceeds unity the system is regenerative and the device will switch into the ON state. This is shown quantitatively below.

Current At J_2

$$I = IM_n\ \alpha_1 + IM_p\ \alpha_2 + I_R$$

$$I = \frac{I_R}{1 - (M_n\ \alpha_1 + M_p\ \alpha_2)}$$

where

I_R = reverse current leakage through J_2
M_n = multiplication constant for electrons
M_p = multiplication constant for holes
α_1 = current gain of NPN transistor
α_2 = current gain of PNP transistor

The multiplication factor M is given by

$$M = \frac{1}{1 - \left(\dfrac{V}{V_A}\right)^N}$$

At voltages approaching the avalanche voltage breakdown, M becomes large. Since α increases with current, M and α both increase until $M_N\ \alpha_1 + M_P\ \alpha_2$ exceeds unity. The device exhibits a region of negative resistance and switches ON. The current that flows is then limited only by the external resistance.

With the addition of a third electrode, called the gate, the α of the NPN transistor can be increased to trigger the device into the ON condition at voltages less than the breakover voltage. The current flowing through J_2 in the case of the triode is shown below

$$I = (I_G + I)\alpha_1 + I\alpha_2 + I_R$$

$$I = \frac{I_G\,\alpha_1 + I_R}{1 - (\alpha_1 + \alpha_2)}$$

where

I_R = reverse current leakage through J_2

I_G = gate current into device

α_1 = current gain of NPN transistor

α_2 = current gain of PNP transistor

These two examples of turn-on are well known and devices utilizing these principles are commercially available.

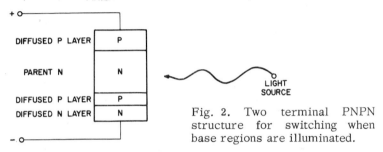

Fig. 2. Two terminal PNPN structure for switching when base regions are illuminated.

Another method for switching a PNPN device from its OFF state to its conducting state is shown in Fig. 2. The device shown is a two-terminal PNPN structure with provisions for illumination of the base regions. It is called the Photoswitch. Light focused on the P and the N base regions will excite electron-hole pairs. This effect is well known and utilized in a number of phototransistors and photoduodiodes such as the Type 1N2175 manufactured by Texas Instruments, Inc. When light is focused on the base region of the PNPN structure, the effect is essentially the same as the application of gate current in the three-terminal structure previously discussed.

The experimental devices were made using an all-diffused structure. The P base width was of the order of 1 mil and the N base was of the order of 4 mils. The dynamic characteristics of such a device are shown in Fig. 3.

The forward breakover voltage under dark conditions for this device was 160 volts. With illumination of 100 lumens per sq ft, as measured with an Eppley thermopile, from a tungsten lamp source operating at approximately 2870 K, the breakover voltage was 90 volts. With illumination of 350 lumens per sq ft, the device has completely switched on with a very low forward voltage drop.

This illumination (350 lumens per sq ft) corresponds to a 60-watt incandescent bulb placed several inches away from the device.

The glass package used for the Photoswitch is shown in Fig. 4. The diameter is 0.080 inch and the length is 0.60 inch. This design provides a low-cost hermetically sealed package. The PNPN wafer used in the device is approximately 0.050 inch in diameter. Typical characteristics of the Photoswitch are as follows:

BV_F	150 volts
PIV	150 volts
I_F	50 mA
I_H	1 mA
V_F @ 50 mA	0.8 volt
I_F (off)	10 microamp. @ 50 volts
I_R (off)	1 microamp. @ 50 volts
Light required	300 lumens/sq ft
to switch on	
(50 volts to 25 mA)	

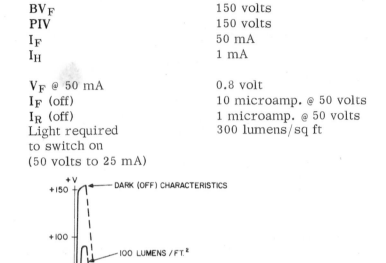

Fig. 3. Curves showing the dynamic characteristics of the Photoswitch.

The spectral response of the Photoswitch has not been measured. It should not, however, be very different than the Type 1N2175 photoduodiode whose maximum sensitivity occurs at 0.9 microns.

Some preliminary measurements were made on the response time of the Photoswitch. As with its big brother, the controlled rectifier, the device will remain in the ON state until the forward current is reduced below the holding current of the device. For switching-time measurements, the forward current through the Photoswitch was adjusted to a value below its holding current. A xenon stroboscopic light was used as the light source to trigger the device. The light duration was less than a microsecond. A Type 931-A photomultiplier tube was used to trigger the oscilloscope with the light source. The turn-on time is of the order of one microsecond. There is a storage time of about 20 microseconds and a long decay time characteristic of a device with high-lifetime silicon in the base layers. In this case, decay time is of the order of 100 microseconds.

There are several advantages and limitations to the Photoswitch. The principal advantage is the high ratio of light current to dark current. Dark current is in the order of 10 microamperes or less, and light current is limited only by the internal dissipation of the

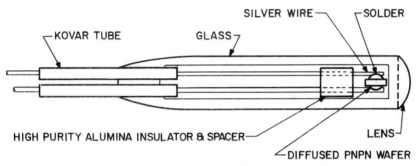

Fig. 4. Cross-sectional diagram of the Photoswitch. The diameter is 0.080 in. and the length is 0.60 in.

device. At room temperatures forward currents in the range of 50 to 100 ma are feasible. One disadvantage of the Photoswitch is its temperature dependence. Since the NPN α has to be high to give the required sensitivity to illumination, the forward breakover voltage decreases rapidly with temperature. This temperature dependence is also a limiting factor on the forward current through the device. With the sensitivity of the device, back bias on the gate would help considerably to reduce the temperature dependence of BV_F. With the present glass package, however, it would be quite difficult to attach a gate electrode to provide back bias without increasing the size of the package. An alternate method for high temperature operation is to increase the 25 C breakover voltage. Data on a typical normal and high-voltage are shown in the accompany-

Breakover Voltage of Typical Normal and High-voltage Photoswitch Units for Various Junction Temperatures.

Junction temperature (deg C)	Breakdown voltage of normal unit (volts)	Breakdown voltage of high-voltage unit (volts)
25	215	1090
50	190	980
75	155	840
100	100	500

ing table. The breakover voltage of the high-voltage unit at 100 C is still in the order of 500 volts. This method could not, of course, be used with the normal two-terminal device where voltage is used to turn the device on.

Several applications for the Photoswitch have been investigated. One such useful application is to control high current silicon controlled rectifiers with light. The Photoswitch can control the gate circuit to control many kilowatts of power. Its small size and its high ratio of light current to dark current make it attractive for punched card readout.

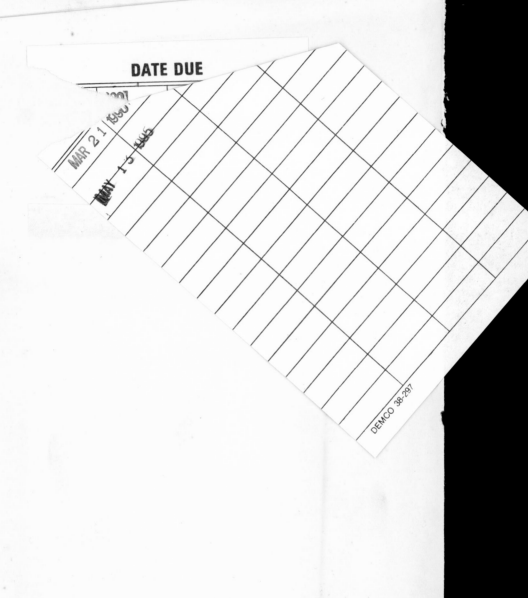

DATE DUE

MAR 21 1950

MAY 15 1965